NUTRITION, EXERCISE
AND
BODY COMPOSITION

Publication Number 574

AMERICAN LECTURE SERIES®

A Monograph in

AMERICAN LECTURES IN SPORTSMEDICINE

Edited by

ERNST JOKL, M.D.

University of Kentucky
Lexington, Kentucky

NUTRITION, EXERCISE
AND
BODY COMPOSITION

By

ERNST JOKL, M.D.
University of Kentucky
Lexington, Kentucky

CHARLES C THOMAS • PUBLISHER
Springfield • *Illinois* • *U.S.A.*

Published and Distributed Throughout the World by
CHARLES C THOMAS • PUBLISHER
BANNERSTONE HOUSE
301-327 East Lawrence Avenue, Springfield, Illinois, U.S.A.
NATCHEZ PLANTATION HOUSE
735 North Atlantic Boulevard, Fort Lauderdale, Florida, U.S.A.

*With THOMAS BOOKS careful attention is given to all details of
manufacturing and design. It is the Publisher's desire to present books
that are satisfactory as to their physical qualities and artistic possibilities
and appropriate for their particular use. THOMAS BOOKS will be true
to those laws of quality that assure a good name and good will.*

Printed in the United States of America
A-2

INTRODUCTION

O F THE THREE MAIN CATEGORIES of adaptation to physical training, viz., those relating to body composition, to the functional responses by the autonomic system, and to the integrative action of the central nervous system, exercise research has hitherto paid attention mainly to the second. With the rapid extension of interest in problems of body composition, a considerable amount of information has become available on the first. As to the third, new insight has recently been afforded through studies of superb performance achievements by athletes who were afflicted with physical handicaps.* The problem of the physiological and pathological interdependence of nutrition, exercise and body composition centers around the modifying influence of physical activity upon the long term effects of nutrition. The issue was first reviewed in a paper read at the International Symposium on Nutrition and Exercise held in Hilversum, Holland in 1962.** A number of important studies have since appeared and were incorporated in this volume. Some of the theoretical conclusions were originally suggested by the observation of correspondingly opposite manifestations of the ergogenic and atherogenic properties of high-calory-high-fat diets in sedentary and physically active subjects, respectively. The morphological data obtained during the Kentucky Physical Fitness Experiment (Chapters II-V) which provide background information as well as the relevant statistical evidence, were summarized in my report at the "Symposium on Body Composition" held by the New York Academy of Sciences in January 1963.***

---

*cp. Ernst Jokl: *The Scope of Exercise in Rehabilitation*. Monograph. Thomas, 1964.
**cp. Nutrition and Athletic Performance. *Netherlands Journal of Nutrition*, 23:11, Nov. 15, 1962.
***Proceedings of the International Conference on Body Composition. The New York Academy of Sciences, New York, 1963.

I express my thanks to Dr. John B. Wells, Jr. and Dr. Jana Parizkova who have made essential contributions to this study, and also acknowledge my indebtedness to Drs. J. K. Alexander, A. R. Behnke, J. Brozek, H. Bruch, E. R. Buskirk, N. Curtius, M. Karvonen, A. Keys, J. Mayer, J. N. Morris, L. R. Pascale, P. I. Randle, T. A. Rogers, I. Starr, A. J. Stunkard, M. Witkowski and I. Yudkin of whose writings I have made use; as well as to the Editors of *The Lancet* who granted permission to quote from two editorial articles published in 1959 and 1963; and to the *Journal of the American Association for Physical and Mental Rehabilitation* who allowed reproduction of some of the material contained in our previously communicated research reports on the Kentucky Physical Fitness Experiment.

E. J.

CONTENTS

Page

Introduction v

Chapter

1. Nutrition and Athletic Performance 3
2. Obesity due to Physical Inactivity 47
3. Exercise, Excess Fat and Body Weight 53
4. The Kentucky Physical Fitness Experiment 72
5. The Effect of Intensive Physical Training upon Body
   Composition and Physical Efficiency of Adolescent Girls. . . . 84
6. Statistical Treatment of Body Measurements in Relation to
   Growth and Physical Training as Modifying Influences. 97

Author Index 109
Subject Index 113

NUTRITION, EXERCISE
AND
BODY COMPOSITION

Chapter 1

NUTRITION AND ATHLETIC PERFORMANCE

ERGOGENIC AND ATHEROGENIC PROPERTIES OF DIETS

OUR CURRENT KNOWLEDGE of diets for champion athletes rests upon two fundamental observations that were made in nutritional studies during Olympic Games; first, that these diets are distinguished by a high caloric content as well as by an abundance of fats and proteins. And secondly, that standards of any nation's athletic efficiency are directly related to its nutritional habits. The relevant evidence was obtained by my colleagues *Karvonen, Kihlberg, Koskela, Noro* and myself at the Helsinki Games in 1952. From this evidence a better understanding has been derived of two major aspects of the science of nutrition in general: of the ergogenic and the atherogenic properties of diet, that is of the effect of diet upon physical efficiency, and of the role which diet plays in the development of the ischemic cardiac diseases.*

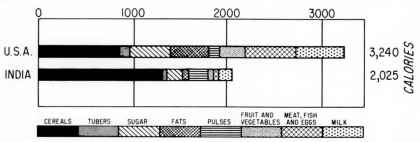

Fig. 1. Nutritional standards in the United States and India

*The term "ischemic cardiac disease" was adopted in 1955 by the World Health Organization (WHO) in reference to pathological conditions of the heart due to impairment of blood and oxygen supply of the myocardium, including angina pectoris, coronary insufficiency, coronary thrombosis, and myocardial infarction.

HEALTH, SOCIO-ECONOMIC STATUS AND PHYSICAL PERFORMANCES

Man can exist on varying diets to which in turn far reaching implications attach. As an example, reference is made to the different

TABLE 1. Olympic Performance Data (A + B) and Selected Vital Statistics (C) for the United States and India
For further detail consult Jokl, Karvonen *et al.*: Sports in the cultural pattern of the world. Helsinki, Finland, 1956

(A) Team Competitions, Point Share

	United States	India
Games playing		
football	5	5
basketball	100	.
field hockey	.	100
water-polo	54	3
Canoeing	65	.
Fencing	95	.
Modern pentathlon	49	.
Yachting	292	.
Cycling	12	12
Equestrian	113	.
Rowing	333	.
Swimming		
4X200 m relay, men	100	.
4X100 m relay, ladies	57	.
Gymnastics		
men	34	.
ladies	2	.
Track and field		
4X100 m relay, men	100	.
4X400 m relay, men	76	.
4X100 m relay, ladies	100	.
Total, men	1428	120
Total, ladies	159	.
Total general	1587	120

(B) Individual Competitions, Point Share

	United States	India
Shooting	408	43
Canoeing, men	157	.
Canoeing, ladies	30	.
Fencing, men	212	.
Fencing, ladies	148	.
Modern pentathlon	133	.
Boxing	645	85
Free style wrestling	423	137
Greco-Roman wrestling	.	.
Weight-lifting	584	22
Cycling	29	4
Equestrian	224	.
Rowing	24	.
Swimming		
men	1372	51
ladies	809	27
Gymnastics		
men	159	—
ladies	63	.
Track and field		
men	3355	148
ladies	241	36
Total, men	7725	490
Total, ladies	1291	63
Total general	9016	553

(C) Vital Statistics

	United States	India
Height (cm)	177	166
Weight (lbs)	161	129
Longevity (years)	70	41
Mortality (per 1000)	9.2	21.8
Infantile mortality (per 1000)	16	47
TBC (per 100,000)	39	232
Income per capita (in U.S. $)	1525	75

nutritional standards in India and in the United States (Fig. 1), each of which is associated with well defined developmental, clinical, economic and physical performance characteristics (Table 1).

The four columns in Figure 2 relate to the diets of the Olympic athletes (1), of the average American citizen of today (2), to the "ideal diet" proposed by *Ancel Keys* (3), and to that of the under-

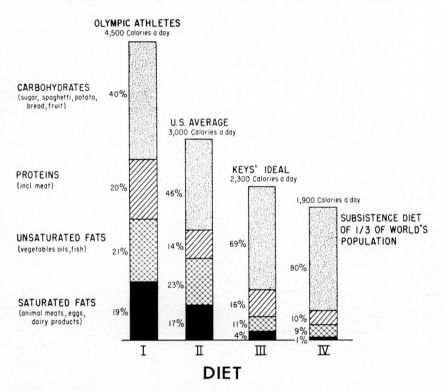

Fig 2. Dietary analyses for Olympic Athletes (1), average American citizens (2), Keys' ideal diet (3), and diet of underprivileged third of the world's population (4)*

---

*The people of North America, Europe, Oceania, and the River Plate countries consume a daily average of 573 g. milk, 152 g. meat, 30 g. eggs, and 34 g. fish. The people of the poorer countries, mostly in Asia, Africa and Latin America, get an average of only 79 g. milk, 30 g. meat, 4 g. eggs, and 24 g. fish daily. Total intakes of protein are 90 g. per head per day (44 g. of animal protein) for the wealthy and 58 g. (only 9 g. from animal sources) for the poorer group. ('The State of Food and Agriculture', 1962. Food and Agriculture Organization, Rome.)

privileged third of the world's population (4). In Figure 3 I have compared diet (III), intended for homo sedentarius Americanus with that of the Olympic athletes (I). Both diets are non-atherogenic; in the first instance because of the intensive physical activity in which champion athletes indulge; in the second, because it is restricted in respect of saturated fats and proteins as well as of calories. The athletes' diet is conducive to the attainment of optimal physical performances. If the same diet were consumed by sedentary subjects it would not by itself exert its ergogenic influence.** Instead, it would lead to obesity and facilitate the development of ischemic heart disease. Athletes are protected from these sequelae as long as they continue with their training. The protection ceases if they become inactive. I have presented ballistocardiographic evidence obtained from former Olympic athletes ten or more years after discontinuation of training showing marked deterioration of myocardial contraction force patterns. By contrast, excellent cardiac tracings were recorded from subjects of corresponding age who had exercised throughout the years. There had been no significant differences in the diet of the two groups (Fig. 4A and B).

Evidently, the atherogenicity of high calory, high fat and high protein diets is nullified by athletic training. The differences in fats and proteins between diets I and III reflect the extent to which muscular exercise modifies the intermediary metabolism of these nutrients. The proportional restriction of carbohydrates in the food consumed by the Olympic athletes suggests the degree to which this category of nutrients is redundant. It is possible that this latter observation has a bearing upon *Yudkin's* theory that high

---

**The significance of the difference between the 2 diets in Fig. 3B extends beyond the field of study from which the evidence has been derived. It touches upon a basic problem to which experimental physiology has hitherto paid but scant aattention, namely to the *identification of functional optima.* In the course of his investigation of hearts of trained and untrained subjects *William Raab* has suggested that only the former's cardiovascular systems are truly normal. He has coined the term "loafer's heart" for the heart of the average untrained person. The classification of patients into "normal" and "diseased" to which clinical medicine adheres does not take into account the vast array of physiological variants that are encountered among "healthy" population groups. Olympic athletes represent a concisely defined sample of "functionally perfect" men and women; it seems reasonable to look upon their diet as ideal nutritional correlate to and prerequisite for the "optimal physiological state."

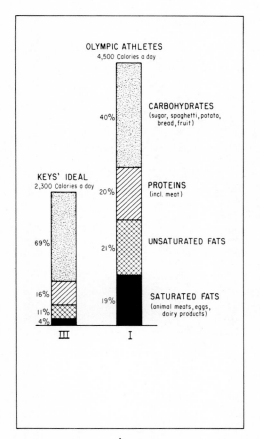

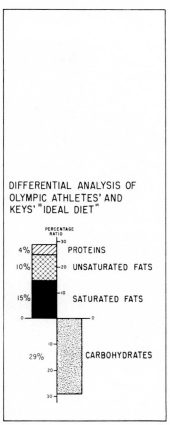

Fig. 3. A. "Ideal diet" for homo sedentarius Americanus (3), and diet of Olympic athletes (1). B. Differential analyses of Olympic athletes and Keys' "ideal diet"

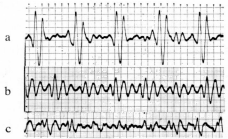

Fig. 4A. Typical ballistocardiograms from (a) Olympic athlete, (b) middle aged trained man, (c) former Olympic athlete after several years of inactivity, showing determining influence upon cardiac force patterns of physical training over diet (from Jokl, E.: "Effect of sports and athletics on the cardiovascular system") (cp. also Diettert).

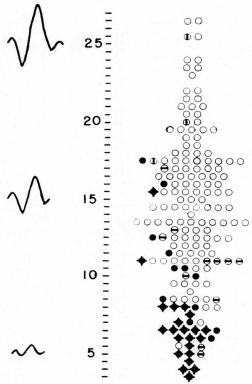

Fig. 4B. The long-term implications of ballistocardiographic amplitudes in respect of their prognostic relevance have been demonstrated in a classical study conducted with middle aged subjects by I. Starr and co-workers. In a statistical analysis of the incidence of heart disease 17 years after the recording of first ballistocardiograms, it was found that high amplitudes are of distinctly favorable and low amplitudes of distinctly un-favorable prognostic significance.

Circles, no heart disease developed; *dots,* those who developed undoubted heart disease; *crosses superimposed* indicate that they died from it; *horizontal bars,* those who developed a doubtful cardiac status; *vertical bars,* those who developed hypertension without evidence of heart disease.

consumption levels of sugar are of the same significance in the pathogenesis of the ischemic heart diseases as high consumption levels of fat. Apparently the role of the various dietary components cannot be conclusively evaluated unless the exercise factor is taken into account.

DIET, BLOOD LIPIDS AND ISCHEMIC HEART DISEASES

Figure 5A correlates coronary mortality and percentage share of calories derived from dietary fat: the incidence of coronary disease is lowest in countries whose diets contain least fat. Levels of blood lipids reflect a similar trend. Though diet is evidently not the only

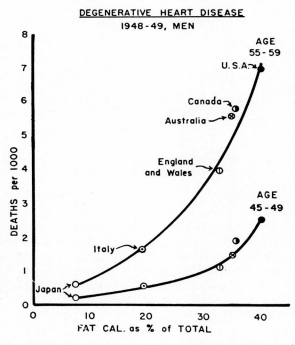

Fig. 5A. Mortality from coronary heart disease. (Categories 93 and 94 in the Revision of 1938, categories 420 and 422 in the Revision of 1948, International List. National vital statistics from official sources. Fat calories as percentage of total calories calculated from national food balance data for 1949 supplied by the Nutrition Division, Food and Agricultural Organization, United Nations.) (From Ancel Keys)

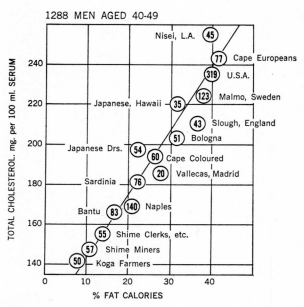

Fig. 5B. An important factor in producing differences in the frequency of coronary heart disease in populations is the proportion of calories in the diet provided by fats. The amount and type of fat influences the blood cholesterol level, which in turn influences the incidence of atherosclerosis and heart disease. In middle age, coronary heart disease is at least ten times as common in the United States as in Japan. (From Ancel Keys: Calories and Cholesterol, *Geriatrics,* May, 1957.)

determinant of the incidence of ischemic heart disease, there is a general tendency for populations who consume a fat rich diet to have high levels of blood lipids* as well as high rates of coronary mortality. The high fat content of their diets places the Olympic athletes on the extreme right of the diagram in Figures 5A and B. However, rates of coronary mortality of physically active subjects are known to be low. Figure 5B shows the correlation between percentage representation in total calory consumption of fat and serum cholesterol.

Keys *et al.* also assessed dietary fats, blood lipids and the incidence of coronary disease of the multiracial population of Cape Town in South Africa. They found significant differences in fat consumption of Bantu, Colored and European subjects. These differences were mirrored in the three groups' blood lipid levels, most markedly so in the older age ranges (Table 2).

Karvonen, Rautanen, Rikkonen and *Kihlberg* obtained lower serum cholesterol values at rest in male and female champion skiers than in untrained subjects (Tables 3a and 3b). The differences were not great. *Rautaharju* et al. estimated the incidence of early coronary changes in a large sample of seemingly healthy middle age subjects. Among the latter were a group of lumber-

---

*The terms "blood lipids" and "blood fats" pertain to a number of correlated biochemical entities whose differential relationship to nutrition, exercise and training will not be discussed in this chapter. Like glucose and the amino acids, lipids are transported throughout the body by the blood, especially by the plasma. For convenience in classification, the following types of compounds are usually considered separately:

(1) Fatty acids esterified with glycerol to form neutral fat.
(2) Free cholesterol (not esterified) and non-esterified fatty acids.
(3) Cholesterol esters of the fatty acids.
(4) Phospholipids of the following three types:
    (a) lecithins, composed of glycerol esterified with two molecules of fatty acid and combined with a molecule of phosphoric acid, which in turn is united with a molecule of the nitrogenous base, choline;
    (b) cephalins, made up of glycerol and two fatty acid molecules, plus phosphoric acid and the nitrogenous base, amino-ethyl alcohol (colamine)
    (c) sphingomyelins, containing no glycerol but composed of a fatty acid, phosphoric acid, choline and another nitrogenous base, sphingosine.
(5) Compounds as yet unidentified, present in relatively small amounts.
Much of the lipid material in human plasma is combined with protein. Two lipoprotein fractions constitute about 10 per cent of the plasma proteins: the alpha-lipoprotein is about 40 per cent lipid, the beta about 75 per cent. The lipid portion consists of phospholipids and cholesterol, largely esterified.

jacks whose occupation necessitates intensive sustained physical work. Their cardiac status was singularly favorable.

The relationhip between blood lipid levels and cardiac status is not consistent. *Karvonen* pointed out that reduction of saturated fats in the diet of patients in a mental hospital was followed by a

TABLE 2. MEAN VALUES FOR SERUM TOTAL AND β LIPOPROTEIN CHOLESTEROL IN SAMPLES OF MEN OF 3 AGE DECADES IN CAPE TOWN, SOUTH AFRICA
(From ANCEL KEYS: "The diet and the development of coronary heart disease," *J. chron. Dis., 4:364, 1956.*

Group	No. men	Diet fat (% cal.)	20—29 years Total	β	30—39 years Total	β	40—49 years Total	β
Bantu	183	17	154.8	113.5	168.8	123.0	168.5	121.3
Colored	102	25	159.6	115.9	194.1	142.5	195.0	145.3
European	129	35—40	203.3	159.2	223.4	175.6	241.8	201.4

TABLE 3a

SERUM CHOLESTEROL LEVELS OF MALE AND FEMALE CHAMPION SKIERS
(From Karvonen, Rautanen, Rikkonen and Kihlberg)

	M e n	W o m e n
Number of subjects	44	15
Cholesterol mg per cent:		
mean	204	194
range	132-307	159-268
st. error of the mean	5.4	8.1
Age years: mean	28.1	24.2
range	21-38	19-29

TABLE 3b

COMPARISON OF FINNISH SKIERS' MEAN SERUM TOTAL CHOLESTEROL VALUES WITH THOSE OF RURAL POPULATION WITHIN THE SAME AGE RANGE
(From Karvonen, Rautanen, Rikkonen and Kihlberg)

Group	Number of Subjects	Serum Cholesterol mg per 100 ml Mean	Standard Error	Significance of Difference
M e n				
Skiers, age 21—38	44	204	5.4	p = 0.01
Rural Finland, age 20—39	283	229	3.1	p = 0.01
W o m e n				
Skiers, age 19—29	15	194	8.1	p = 0.05
Rural Finland, age 20—29	16	226	8.9	

reduction of blood cholesterol levels but not by a decline of rates of mortality from ischemic heart disease.

THE ANTI-ATHEROGENIC INFLUENCE OF PHYSICAL TRAINING

"All animals that are excessively fat age rapidly."
(Aristotle, "De partibus animalium," II/4, 651 b., Oxford ed., 1912)

Exercise seems to exert a more determining influence upon cardiac status than diet. Although diet influences the concentration of blood lipids it is doubtful whether the favorable long-term effects of exercise upon the cardiovascular system are necessarily reflected in a corresponding drop of the concentration of blood lipids. Physically active persons may consume a fat rich diet but enjoy protection from the atherogenicity which it displays in sedentary subjects. Finnish champion skiers who continue to exercise live 6-8 years longer than subjects who lead a sedentary life (Fig. 6). The results of *Pomeroy* and *White's* analysis of mortality figures for a group of 355 former football players, though not conclusive,

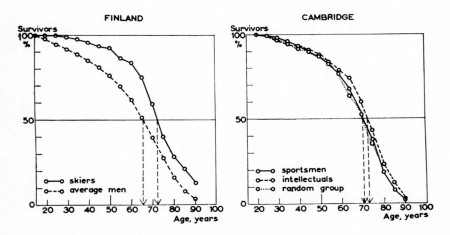

Fig. 6. Sustained physical training characterized the life habits of Finnish champion skiers who lived significantly longer than the general male population of Finland (after Karvonen). By contrast, no effect upon longevity was found in Sir Alan Rook's study of data pertaining to former students of Cambridge University in England who had rowed in the famous boat race during their twenties but discontinued with their training after completing their academic courses.

point in the same direction. *Morris* et al. in England and *Brunner* in Israel have studied the incidence of ischemic heart disease in physically active and in sedentary populations. Their findings lend strong support to the hypothesis that exercise is the most significant among the known non-genetic modifiers of the pathogenesis of ischemic heart disease. The validity of the reverse assumption, viz. that lack of activity facilitates coronary disease is born out by the close parallelism between rising rates of coronary mortality and of radio and T.V. licenses in England (Fig. 7).

The high concentration of blood lipids in sedentary subjects who consume fat rich diets is due to the fact that they thus overload the transport system for lipids from gut to liver to subcutaneous fat depots. Intensive physical activity obviates such overloading because dietary fats are promptly metabolized during exercise. As will be shown presently, the muscle derives kinetic energy from fat

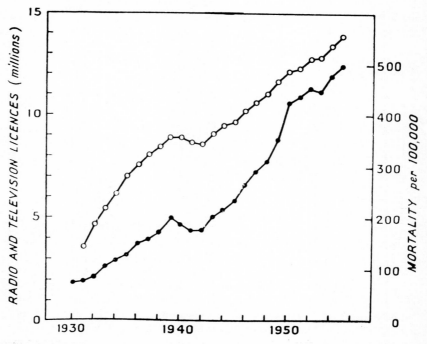

Fig. 7. Trends of coronary mortality and number of radio and T.V. licenses in Great Britain. (After John Yudkin.)

at a favorable ratio between mechanical yield and heat production.*
How training affects the transport system for lipids is not yet understood. It is true that exercise lowers blood fat levels. But this does not explain how training** influences the intermediary fat metabolism over longer periods.

A comparison of Tables 2 and 3 shows that blood fat levels in the poor Bantu population in Cape Town were lower than in the Finnish skiing champions. While the latter were free to eat as much fat as they liked, the former's diet was deficient in fats and thus in ergogenicity. No champion athletes have yet come from South Africa's underprivileged Bantu society though the athletic status of representatives of the "European" section of South Africa who eat a fat rich diet and whose blood lipids levels are normal or high, is excellent.***

THE ROLE OF DIETARY PROTEINS

Considerable physiological significance attaches to the observation of high consumption levels of protein in the Olympic athletes' diet.

A hundred years ago C. Voit introduced the concept of what is now called "the labile body protein fraction." When a subject on a high protein diet is suddenly changed to a diet containing as little as 50 g. of protein, he comes into nitrogen balance again after an interval of a few days. During this period he loses protein. If he then returns to a high protein diet he will once more establish a nitrogen balance after an interval during which he is laying down protein. The amount of protein lost or gained may be as much as 5 per cent of total body protein. The "labile" protein fraction must

---

*The percentual contribution to the cardiac metabolism by non-carbohydrates and carbohydrates respectively is as follows: *Non-Carbohydrates*—Fatty Acids 58%, Amino Acids 5.6%, Ketone Bodies 4.3%; *Carbohydrates*—Pyruvates 0.5%, Lactate 14.5%, Glucose 17.1%:

**The term "exercise" refers to single physiological performances, e.g., short-term neuro-muscular events. The term "training" refers to long-term processes which are synthesized, so to speak, from frequent repetitions of single exercise activities. Exercise and training are separate conceptual entities which, however, belong to one and the same cause and effect circuit.

***The question how far and in what manner the ergogenic and atherogenic effects of saturated and unsaturated fats differ cannot be discussed within the context of this paper. Because of its categorical importance for the formulation of a theory of the relationship between nutrition and exercise, it will be given special consideration elsewhere.

be distinguished from "essential" cell protein whose loss leads to wasting and ill health.

The question arises whether labile protein contributes to an individual's physical performance capacity or increases his resistance to infections.

Experiences with champion athletes prove that the first of these questions must be answered in the affirmative. The fact that laboratory studies as well as observations with subjects who indulge in moderate exercise do not necessarily show a negative urinary nitrogen balance does not detract from the validity of this statement. E.g., in 1899, Fick and Wislicenus climbed the Faulhorn in Switzerland which is 1956 meters high and found that their output of urinary nitrogen was similar to that during an ordinary

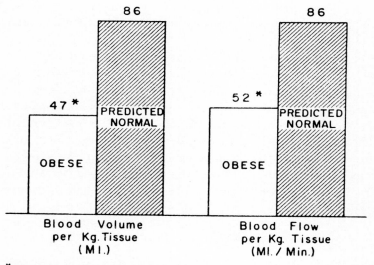

BLOOD VOLUME AND FLOW PER UNIT BODY WEIGHT
IN OBESITY

Fig. 8. An important study which has thrown light upon the role of obesity in facilitating the pathogenesis of the cardiovascular diseases has been made by J. K. Alexander *et al.*, who compared blood volume, cardiac output and distribution of systemic blood flow in normal and obese subjects. They found that blood volume and blood flow per kg. tissue in highly obese subjects was significantly decreased.

day. Newer laboratory studies have yielded similar results.

Altogether, laboratory studies with animals such as the forced swimming experiment with rats by Holt *et al.,* or the ergometric performance analyses with human subjects by Mellerowicz do not allow conclusions applicable to champion athletes under competition. "Record physiology" has rules of its own as A. H. Frucht has convincingly shown.

As regards the second question: no modifications of a physiologically adequate diet are capable of increasing resistance to infections. In his survey of human nutrition in 1962, *Glatzel* emphasized that our knowledge of the effect of exhaustive exercise upon protein metabolism is still sketchy. Similarly *Schimert* et al. in their monograph on coronary heart disease (1960) point out that the question of the pathogenetic role of protein rich diets cannot yet be conclusively answered. Again, it seems that the issue requires consideration not only of the nutritional but also of the exercise factor. Until a few years ago *Hindhede's* views that "large amounts of animal protein in the diet are poison to the human organism" had serious followers. The results of the 1952 Olympic nutrition survey leave no doubt that such an assertion is untenable. On the contrary, an abundance of biologically high class dietary proteins seems to be a prerequisite for the attainment of the morphological and functional adaptations upon which athletic excellence depends. More particularly, there is no evidence for the assumption that in physically active subjects high protein intake exerts an atherogenic effect. *Keys* has pointed out that the diet of most populations known to be free from ischemic heart disease is low in animal protein. But a diet which satisfies metabolic minimum requirements in sedentary individuals is not eo ipso suitable for champion athletes. The fact that every poodle is a dog does not prove that every dog is a poodle.

CALORIC INTAKE AND THERMODYNAMIC OUTPUT

As regards the high caloric intake levels of Olympic athletes it is important to remember that the laws of thermodynamics are universally valid in physiology. The 1500 or more calories which we consume at a banquet need for their expenditure a walk of 20 miles or swimming of 3 hours or cycling for 6 hours. Of course, most persons who attend banquets do nothing of the sort. Thus their energy expenditure remains unchanged and the surplus calories are, therefore, deposited as excess fat.

Because of their high energy expenditure Olympic runners, swimmers etc. have virtually no excess fat even though their body weight may be high. *Keller* has presented comparative evidence relating to the issue. Of course the energy expenditure of champion athletes is very great. The training program of middle distance men such as *Elliot* and *Snell* before the Rome Games in 1960 included running of more than 100 miles per week, in addition to other forms of exercise such as calisthenics, swimming and weight lifting. Some of our best swimmers cover up to 6 miles every day.

THE FUEL OF MUSCULAR EXERCISE*

In 1866, *Pettenkofer* and *Voit* showed that mechanical work did not increase protein metabolism. In 1907, *Fletcher* and *Hopkins* revealed the relation of lactic acid to muscular activity and thus emphasized the importance of carbohydrates in muscle. Subsequently *Meyerhof* and *Hill* showed the close relation of carbohydrate breakdown and lactic acid formation with muscle tension and liberation of heat. Though the utilization of fats in muscular work was not questioned it was believed that fats are first converted into carbohydrates and stored in the muscles as glycogen. Carbohydrates were thus considered as "prime fuel" of muscle. This view has recently been challenged. Studies of non-esterified fatty acids in the plasma, commonly called N.E.F.A., have shown that unlike other lipid components this fraction is relatively little affected by a fatty meal. Though its concentration in plasma is only between 0.5 and 1.0 m-mole per liter, its rate of turnover is about 40 times greater than that of glucose. Since a molecule of N.E.F.A. provides on oxidation more than 3 times as much energy as a molecule of glucose, N.E.F.A. could easily supply the necessary fuel for muscular exercise. In 1944 *Stetten and Boxer* using deuterium showed that in rats on a high-carbohydrate diet only about 3 per cent of the dietary glucose was handled as glycogen and at least 10 times as much was used to synthesize fatty acids as to synthesize glycogen. *Wertheimer* and *Shapiro* have been

---

*cp. Editorial, *The Lancet*, September 5, 1959.

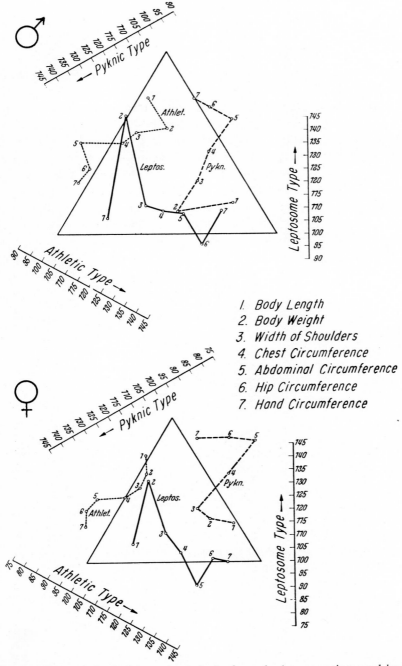

Fig. 9. Determining influence upon body form, body proportions and body composition of physical training over hereditary patterns and diet. Differences of body measurements from trained and untrained men and women of leptosome, athletic and pyknic body build. (The straight lines of triangles represent norm values obtained from psychiatric hospital patients; the "numbered" lines the values relating to the athletes.)

pioneers in demonstrating that adipose tissue is not simply a stable store of fat, but an actively metabolizing tissue capable of converting carbohydrate into fat and with a rapid rate of turnover of its chemical constituents. The opinion is now rapidly gaining ground that the major portion of the dietary carbohydrate is converted immediately to fat in the adipose tissues. During muscular exercise it is mobilized directly as N.E.F.A. which is carried to the working muscles. During transit in the blood N.E.F.A. is loosely bound to serum-albumin. Thus, fat rather than carbohydrate now seems to be the "prime fuel" of muscle. The present view is that carbohydrate is the one fuel immediately available in muscle, and its breakdown to lactic acid provides the energy for any burst of activity. But this mechanism is probably responsible for no more than a small fraction of the energy utilized

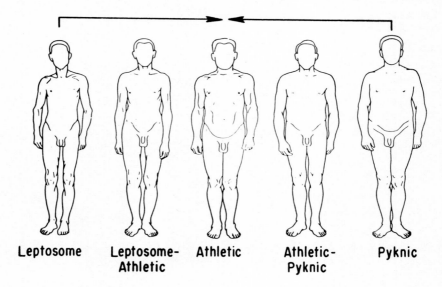

| Leptosome | Leptosome-
Athletic | Athletic | Athletic-
Pyknic | Pyknic |

Fig. 10. Under the influence of training, the wings of the distribution field of normal physiques move toward the center. 30 years ago, Arnold showed that during a two years' physical education teachers course the percentage ratio of "pure" athletic types increased from 30.3 to 50.5. At the same time "pure" leptosome and "pure" pyknic physiques virtually "disappeared."

*Margaria, R.: A Historical Review of the Physiology of Oxygen Debt and Steady State in Relation to Lactic Acid Formation and Removal. *Medicina Dello Sport, III*: 6, July 1963, 637-657.

in long-continued muscular work. The heart muscle can extract from the blood enough fat to account for 70 per cent of the oxygen uptake. Plasma from the veins of exercising muscles contains significantly less N.E.F.A. than that from the veins of resting muscles. There can no longer be any doubt that the non-esterified fatty acids are directly utilized as fuel during muscular exercise.

THE EFFECT OF EXERCISE UPON NON-ESTERIFIED FATTY ACIDS (N.E.F.A.) AND TRIGLYCERIDES IN BLOOD

Though people engaged in heavy physical work tend to have lower serum cholesterol values, the differences between them and those from sedentary subjects are insignificant. Similarly insignificant results were obtained in longitudinal follow-up analyses of serum cholesterol during periods of rest and training.

Two fractions of blood lipids are directly related to energy expenditure, namely non-esterified fatty acids and triglycerides whose concentration determines plasma turbidity after a fatty meal. It is reduced after exercise. This observation is of special interest because abnormalities in triglyceride metabolism are present in a large number of patients with coronary disease.

Nikkila and Konttinen of Helsinki collected samples of serum from 40 healthy young soldiers before as well as 4 and 6 hours after a fat rich meal. During the postprandial period 20 of the 40 subjects rested in bed; while the other 20 marched over a distance of 16 km., each carrying a 8 kg. pack and a gun weighing 4.6 kg.

Figure 11 shows higher serum triglyceride levels in the resting subjects 4 hours after the meal; Figure 12 summarizes corresponding changes in plasma concentration of non-esterified fatty acids. The divergences were of a different kind as well as greater than those pertaining to the triglycerides. A three-fold increase occurred in the exercising group while in the resting group there had been only a slight rise. As regards serum cholesterol levels (Fig. 13) the fatty meal combined with the vigorous physical activity exerted no immediate effect; but under basal conditions total serum cholesterol as well as the α and β lipoprotein cholesterol fractions decreased slightly.

The concentration of plasma triglyceride following a meal is determined by its rate of influx from the intestine and by its rate of clearance from the circulation. The effect of vigorous physical exercise in abolishing the post-prandial rise in plasma triglyceride is due to accelerated removal of neutral fat from the circulation and to the discharge into the circulation of heparinoids and lipase as well as to stimulation of the glucose metabolism.

Ample utilization of free fatty acids during exercise by heart and skeletal muscle has been demonstrated. Whether skeletal muscle can also extract triglyceride fatty acids from plasma is not known.

The Finnish authors explain the rise of plasma nonesterified fatty acids during exercise as follows:

> The increased muscular activity accelerates the extraction of plasma N.E.F.A. by muscle, and at first, this leads to a decrease of plasma N.E.F.A.; at the same time, the lipolytic mechanism of adipose tissue is activated—probably by the adrenergic stimulation and release of catecholamines known to be produced by muscular work. The resulting mobilization of N.E.F.A. first balances the rapid utilization, and then exceeds it; a rise of plasma N.E.F.A. follows. After the exercise, plasma N.E.F.A. falls, but it apparently remains at a level which corresponds with the degree of caloric deficit, for the same level is reached in a resting subject after more protracted starvation.

To summarize, *exercise diminishes the post-prandial lipemia and thus exerts a retarding influence upon the increased concentration of blood lipids, upon the acceleration of blood coagulation, the inhibition of fibrinolysis, the decrease of tissue oxygen tension and the reduction of coronary blood flow in healthy people.*

The relationship between carbohydrate and fat metabolism in as far as they are involved in the release of mechanical energy through the muscular system in exercise has been reviewed by Randell et al. who speak of a "glucose fatty-acid cycle." The essential features of the interactions between glucose and fatty acid metabolism in muscle and adipose tissue which are fundamental to the control of glucose and fatty acid concentrations in the blood, and of insulin sensitivity are

(1)   the restrictions imposed on glucose metabolism in muscle by the release for oxidation of more fatty acids derived from muscle or adipose tissue glycerides (Fig. 14), and

(2)   those imposed on release of fatty acids from glycerides by uptake of glucose (Fig. 15).

LIMITATIONS OF QUANTITATIVE APPROACH

Quantitative analyses of intake and output of energy equivalents do not suffice for the elucidation of the physiological implications of the problem of nutrition and athletics. Abundance of food is a prerequisite not only for the payment of the cost of short-term expenditures of energy but also for the long-term structural changes of an athlete's physique with training. Though genetic features modify their scope, their nature is ubiquitously defined. The anatomical laws underlying these changes presuppose considera-tion of a nonquantitative kind whose nutritional prerequisites are not yet fully understood. Figure 9 shows a number of typical differences of body measurements between trained and untrained men and women of leptosome, athletic and pyknic body build. Also it must be realized that different kinds of athletic training lead to different bodily adjustments. Sports requiring the display of strength elicit a marked increase in body bulk; while feats of endurance lead to special adjustments of the circulatory and respiratory systems.*

The majority of adults maintain a given physique virtually un-changed over some length of time, often over months and years. E.g., though food supply in the United States is practically un-limited, obesity is present in not more than one third of its sedentary population. In other words, not everyone who eats more than necessary becomes fat. Moreover, those who eat too much and do become fat reach in due course a morphological equilibrium even if they continue to consume an overabundant diet. The concept

---

*The erroneous assumption that the quantitative methods which experimental physiology employs in the analysis of biological phenomena suffice for the study of exercise has forced the science of athletics into a Procrustean bed. That the situation which has thus been brought about in physical education is altogether incongruous is shown by a critical survey of the so called "fitness tests" that are currently in vogue. All of these tests presuppose repetition in the trained state of a given set of movements that can be performed by untrained subjects. Only very simple movements comply with this condition which precludes the identification of essential qualitative aspects of neuromuscular learning and thus of the progressive scale of *acquired* motor skills. If the same principle were applied in the evaluation of *musical* performances, all classical compositions would have to be discarded since no beginner can play them. On the other hand if like in the "physical fitness tests" we were to confine ourselves also in music to repetitions of the same performances before and after training, all considerations of technique and esthetics would have to be disregarded. This is what the contemporary research approach to athletics implies. Vice versa, nutrition and exercise cannot be fully comprehended in terms of biochemistry and thermodynamics.

of homeostasis is applicable not only in physiology but also in anatomy. Many of the regulatory mechanisms that are involved in the maintenance of the constancy of individual physiques are known. However, we are unable to explain how intensive physical training patterns body structures, why in the presence of an un-

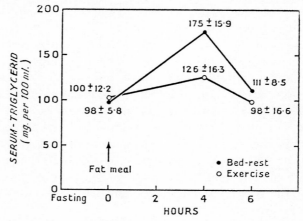

Fig. 11. Mean serum triglyceride levels before and after a fatty meal in resting and exercising subjects.

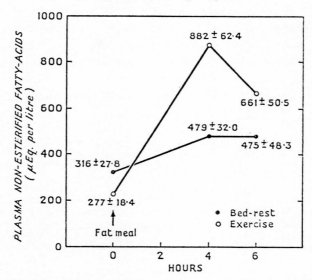

Fig. 12. Mean plasma non-esterified fatty acid concentrations in the same subjects.

restricted diet the maintenance through training of an athlete's physical performance standards stabilizes his physique, and why differences in food consumption between individual champion athletes of identical efficiency are not necessarily reflected in corresponding differences of their physiques.

Provided that no dietary restrictions are imposed, *intensive physical training is the most effective regulator of any given athlete's body composition and body proportions* within the limits of his genetic makeup (Figs. 10 and 11).

The impersonal intelligence of language has given expression to this relationship between food intake, body structure, and functional efficiency by refering to the athlete at the height of his powers as being in "form"; while discontinuation of training leads to "loss of form." Intensive physical training can also counteract some of the trends towards changes in physique and function with advancing years. The difference in "form" of the 25 years old wrestling champion and 30 years later (Fig. 17) is not so much due to "aging" as to the fact that he had discontinued training and thus "lost his form." Altogether trained men and women re-

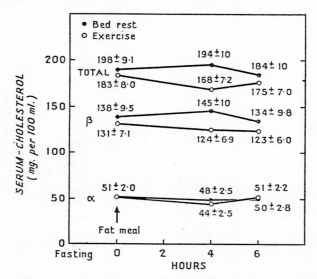

Fig. 13. Mean serum levels of total cholesterol, α-lipoprotein cholesterol, and β-lipoprotein cholesterol in the same subjects. (After Nikkild and Konttinen.)

tain their form even if the caloric content of their food exceeds their energy expenditure through exercise.* Nutrition is but one of the several determinants of athletic performance. *The body has at its disposal means other than exercise to regulate its thermodynamic budget.* Otherwise it would be unable to keep its morphological pattern constant over extended periods.**

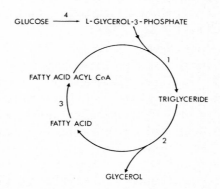

Fig. 14. Glucose fatty-acid cycle, tissue phase. 1) Esterification, 2) Lipolysis, 3) Fatty-acid activation, 4) Glycerol phosphate synthesis.

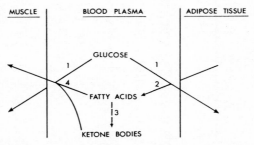

Fig. 15. Glucose fatty-acid cycle, blood phase. 1) Uptake of glucose by muscle and adipose tissue. 2) Release of fatty acids from adipose tissue to plasma albumin. 3) Formation of ketone bodies from fatty acids by liver, 4) Uptake of fatty acids and ketone bodies of muscle.

---

*The issue is well exemplified in the observation that contrary to widespread belief it is not possible to achieve "spot" reducing of excess fat in overweight subjects through exercise. cp. Schade *et al.*

**cp. editorial on "Hypermetabolism" in *Lancet*, p. 1317, Dec. 22, 1962.

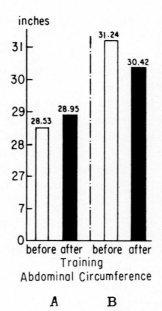

Fig. 16. Effect of intensive physical training upon abdominal circumference. Since in pyknic subjects training causes a greater reduction of excess fat than increase of lean body tissue; while in leptosome the adaptive proportions are reversed; physical training leads in the former to a decrease, in the latter to an increase of abdominal circumference.

SERUM LIPIDS AND ENZYMES

The validity of the thesis first presented in 1962 that intensive sustained physical training tends to nullify the atherogenic effects of a high calory, high fat diet was corroborated in 1963 by Calvy, Cady, Mufson, Nierman and Gertler. These authors undertook a study with young trainees in the U.S. Marine Corps to ascertain "whether a high caloric diet, of which fats and carbohydrates form the major portion, remains potentially pathogenic if sufficient vigorous exercise is engaged in to catabolize most or all of the diet."

For a period of 6 months hitherto untrained recruits participated in a program of rigorous physical exercise coupled with an intake of 4,500 calories (of which 45% was fat). The subjects' weight, blood pressure, serum total cholesterol, lipid phosphorus, uric acid, triglycerides, isocitric dehydrogenase (ICDH), malic dehydrogenase (MDH) and lactic dehydrogenase (LDH) were studied before and after training.

The diet included milk ad lib (3.3 pints average/man daily). Dairy products were plentiful in the form of butter, ice cream (4 oz. [113.3 gm] daily), cheese, eggs (two to three eggs five times a week). The caloric intake of each recruit averaged 4,500 calories of which fats contributed 2,025 calories (225 gm), carbohydrates 2,025 calories (506 gm) and proteins, 450 calories (112 gm).

In the beginning, the training involved 16 hours of rigorous activity, including a five mile forced march daily or an equivalent effort around the obstacle course. The trainees engaged in night maneuvers, bivouac, and other infantry activities. During the later stages of the training exercise requirements were further increased.

The results of the Kentucky Physical Fitness Exeriment (p. 72ff) allow the assumption that the trainees studied by Calvy *et al.,* lost excess fat and gained lean tissue. Thus the finding that "there was far less weight gain than one could expect" seems well explained. Blood pressure, serum cholesterol, serum phosphor lipid and serum uric acid remained unaffected by the training. Serum triglycerides increased from 42 mg per cent to 91 mg per cent, a fact of special interest in connection with the data adduced by Nikkila *et al.* (p. 21).

Calvy *et al.,* hypothesize that exercise promotes the oxidation of fats, including cholesterol. They also point out that the coagulation-fibrinolysis equilibrium is affected by exercise and diet, and that the trend toward increase of clotting and inhibition of fibrinolysis after a meal replete with fats is counteracted by exercise. Blood clotting was found to be prolonged and fibrinolysis enhanced after exercise.

"CONSTITUTIONAL PREDISPOSITION"

Nature and scope of the formative influence of exercise depend upon the physical type of the trainee. In thin, leptosome subjects gain of lean tissue is the predominant feature. They thus move from the left wing towards the "athletic" middle of the distribution field in Figure 10. Conversely, in the flabby pyknic, loss of excess fat is the most decisive bodily adjustment. He therefore, shifts from the right wing towards the center. Though intensive physical training invariably causes loss of excess fat and gain of lean tissue, the two processes of adaptation are differently proportioned in accordance with somato-typical variants. In other words, the same physical training regime causes categorically identical trends of adjustments of body composition with predictable quantitative modification. The crucial point is that the influence upon physique of abundant diets can be overruled by exercise.

This observation is of major importance for the evaluation of the role of "constitutional types" in the pathogenesis of the ischemic cardiac diseases. The current view among clinicians is that the pyknic-athletic type according to Kretschmer or the so-called ectomorph-mesophorphic type according to Sheldon is genetically predisposed towards coronary heart diseases. Whether the issue in fact relates to genotypic determinants or to the phenotypic problem of obesity is doubtful. The statistical evidence adduced by Armstrong, Dublin, Bonneth and Marks points in the latter direction. Reduction of excess fat reduced rates of mortality from the degenerative cardio-vascular diseases and vice versa. The extent to which obesity represents a burden upon the circulatory system has been demonstrated by J. K. Alexander *et al.* Schimert computed a ratio of 46.6 per cent of pyknic to 32.2 per cent of leptosome among male patients with athero- and arteriosclerosis; with a corresponding ratio of 67.8 per cent and 22.2 per cent among female patients. Similar findings have been reported by Gertler *et al.,* and by Spain *et al.,* who used Sheldon's classification.

Burkhardt found in 1232 autopsies a predominance of early degenerative arterial changes in pyknic subjects. According to Gertler and White body bulk is a more relevant factor in the facilitation of ischemic disease than body weight. The fact that in patients thus afflicted significant elevations of beta-lipoproteins were noted in the blood strongly points towards the conclusions that constitutional influences cannot be the sole and probably even not the decisive causative element since "mesomorphic" athletes and other persons who are physically active throughout their lives do not show high blood fat levels while "endomorphic" patients with coronary heart disease show a tendency towards high blood levels. Again, *exercise is likely to be a more determinant factor than genetic stigmata.* We must await the results of analyses of data derived from comparative studies with physically inactive and physically active populations of the kind now undertaken by Brunner, Karvonen, and J. N. Morris. The latter's findings indicate nature and extent of modification of genetic trends through physical activity, independent of diet (Bramwell).

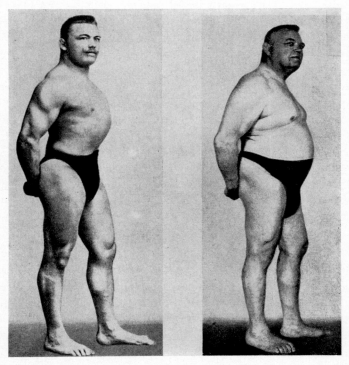

Fig. 17. Effect of discontinuation of physical training upon "form" of former champion athlete who had access to unrestricted diet throughout his life. The difference in physique at age 25 when the subject was holder of several championships in wrestling, and 30 years later, was due primarily to the fact that he had discontinued with his training (after Curtius).

ENVIRONMENTAL DETERMINANTS OF ATHLETIC EFFICIENCY

Table 4 summarizes the results of the statistical analysis of caloric consumption levels of the nations who sent teams to the

TABLE 4

OLYMPIC PARTICIPATION AND ACHIEVEMENT OF NATIONS ON DIFFERENT LEVELS OF
CALORIC CONSUMPTION

Calories Per Head Per Day	Popula- tions in Millions	Participa- tion	Participa- tion Rate	Points	Point Rate	Point Level
1500—1999	432	40	0.09	610	1.4	15.3
2000—2499	749	397	0.53	8,709	11.6	21.9
2500—2999	82	264	3.24	5,936	72.7	22.5
3000—3499	232	969	4.17	29,324	126.1	30.3

Participations: Number of participations from a given country
Point Share: Number of points collected by a country
Participation Rate: Number of participations per million inhabitants
Point Rate: Number of points collected per million inhabitants
Point Level: Average number of points per participation

A striking relationship appears when participation and achievement in Olympic Games are evaluated against caloric consumption levels of the different nations. Table 4 shows that the nations eating little are poorly represented. As the amount of food consumed increases, participation and number of points collected in the athletic contests rise concomitantly. Supporting this finding, the point level of individual athletes was the better, the higher the mean caloric consumption of their home countries. The discovery of such a relationship between caloric consumption and athletic achievement is one of the most important results of this survey. It reminds of the intimate dependence of performance on the adequacy of the physiological mechanisms of the body.

1952 Olympic Games. Though Olympic competitors from all over the world have today access to unrestricted diets, athletic performances nevertheless reflect the general socio-economic environment of the participants' home country. I have dealt elsewhere with the reasons for this interesting phenomenon.* Physical efficiency depends upon many prerequisites of which nutrition, control of infectious diseases, general education and training are the most important. The effect upon athletic efficiency of loss of adaptation energy due to infectious diseases show themselves *collectively* in that the athletic situation in societies thus afflicted is inferior (cp. Table 4); but it is more than probable that they will be reflected also *individually*. When following the establishment of his world record in pole vaulting in 1962 of 16 ft. 3/4 in., John Uelses had to be hospitalized with influenza it took him 2 months to regain his form. Similar instances are known to every coach. The influence even of the best diet upon physical efficiency is nullified by infectious dis-

*Jokl: *Medical Sociology and Cultural Anthropology* of Sport and Physical Education. Thomas, 1964.

eases, though often, of course, only temporarily. But it is a general rule that neither physical training nor nutrition bestow upon the athlete an enhanced immunological status.

"A good diet provides no protection against the great infectious diseases: smallpox, plague, typhus, cholera, and yellow fever do not spare the well-fed rich. The specific immune responses to infections are not closely dependent on diet. It is common in Africa and in Asia to find patients with a low level of plasma-albumin (a good indication of an inadequate protein intake) but with a high level of gammaglobulins which carry the protective antibodies. When there is a shortage of aminoacids for synthesis of tissue proteins, the supply for the formation of antibodies seems to receive priority. Apparently only when protein reserves are greatly reduced and tissue wasting has become severe is the resistance to infections significantly reduced. But even in the very poor of Madras, many of whom are obviously undernourished, W. Fox (Lancet, 1962 II, 413,473) has shown that it is possible to treat tuberculosis effectively and to prevent its spread in family contacts by chemotherapy alone, with no improvements in the diet or in other environmental factors. There is no epidemiological evidence to support the view that a diet contaaining 100 g. of protein provides a better protection against infectious disease than one containing only 50 g." (Protein Stores. Editorial, *The Lancet,* April 13, 1963.)*

*The mutual relationship of the above mentioned and possibly other determinants of athletic efficiency is not yet fully understood. To wit, attention is drawn to a conspicuous item in table 1 (A), that India won the field hockey tournament in 1952. Though the overall athletic performance standards of the United States were greatly superior to those of India, in this Olympic event the position was reversed. The fact that the Indian Olympic champion hockey players' physical, nutritional, health, social and economic status was incomparably better than that of the Indian population as a whole does not fully explain their success since the same preferential status characterized the entire Indian Olympic team which, however, did as a whole not nearly so well at Helsinki as their hockey players. On the other hand, the generally superior physical, nutritional, health, social and economic status of the United States was not reflected in their representatives' performances in the Olympic field hockey tournament. Field hockey is an extremely popular sport in India and Pakistan. At the Olympic Games in Rome in 1960 Pakistan won the hockey tournament against India by one goal to nil. The number of men who play field hockey in the United States is negligible. It is quite possible that Asians possess special neuro-motor endowments that find expression in their outstanding field hockey performances. That ethnic factors may determine athletic efficiency was originally suggested by the conspicuously high success ratios of black athletes from the United States and the British Commonwealth in track and field competitions.

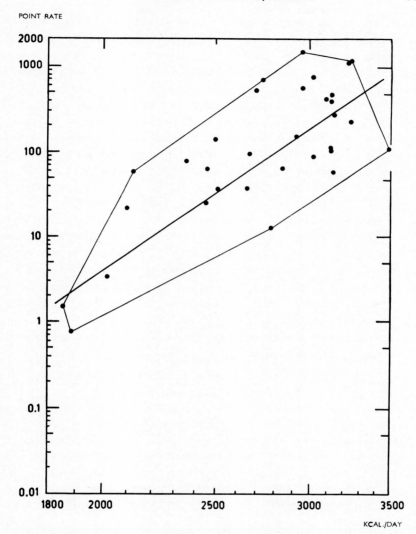

POINT RATE

KCAL./DAY

Fig. 18. Point rate (y) as plotted against the average caloric consumption per day (x). The straight line expresses the regression equation: log y $\underline{s}$ constant $+$ 9.47 log. $\times$. A definite positive correlation is observable.

NOTATION OF MOVEMENTS

Finally I like to comment on the question why important quantitative aspects of the relationship between nutrition and athletic training have so long remained unrecognized. Most laboratory studies so far undertaken in this sector have been confined to physical activities such as running on the treadmill or cranking a handle or working on a bicycle ergometer. Needless to say, these relatively undifferentiated forms of exercise are not comparable with those that are involved in the majority of athletic sports. It is therefore quite inappropriate to assume that the results of such laboratory studies can provide comprehensive information about the physiological implications of sport and athletics. Moreover, the term exercise as used in the current clinical literature is often lacking definition. The situation is similar to that relating to the use of the term "fever" during the first half of the 19th century. The high level of methodological skill that is now generally demanded in the biological sciences is not reflected throughout in the research procedures that are currently applied to human movements in their great diversity. *There is an urgent need for physiology and medicine to elaborate a system of notation of movements.* Only thus can the variants of motor performances in dancing and playing, track and field athletics, wrestling and gymnastics become amenable to analysis and interpretation.

The great British mathematician *H. Levy* has stated the problem in its categorical relevance:

> Science has a dual history. It is the tale of the birth of men with great powers of abstraction, and it is the story of the evolution of languages peculiarly adapted to these abstractions. Our heritage from Newton would have been a much poorer thing but for the differential calculus, as our indebtedness to Einstein is enriched by the tensor notation. What does the development of organic chemistry not owe to the interlocking of Dalton's atomic theory with the synthetic possibilities suggested by graphical formulae? Notation is indeed the very lifeblood of Science.

> Without a musical notation how could the great masters have left a permanent record of their creations, or even conceived detailed and elaborate symphonies? Thought and experience have ever striven for a language rich in expression as an adequate channel for communication; and so in music a notational scheme for precise tonic description was inevitable, and once achieved the way was open for a magnificent outburst of musical art on a grand scale.

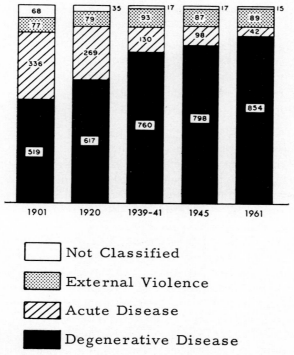

	68		35		17		17		15

Not Classified

External Violence

Acute Disease

Degenerative Disease

Fig. 19. Chances per thousand, at birth, of eventually dying from degenerative disease, acute disease, or external violence, Unted States, 1901-1961. Irrespective of the pathogenetic influence of high calory—high fat diet, exercise is capable of reducing rate and incidence of degenerative diseases, primarily of the cardiovascular system. The extent of the prophylactic efficacy of exercise is tentatively indicated in Karvonen's longevity study (cp. Fig. 6).

He would be bold who would deny the possibility of a similar advance in the art and science of movement, once the kinetics of body and limbs had been suitably notated.

"STRESS"

The issue is of decisive relevance for the study of the two key aspects of the physiology of nutrition and exercise with which I have dealt, i.e., of the ergogenic and atherogenic effects of diets. The ergogenic aspect is frequently discussed as being representative of one of many situations to which a number of writers now refer with the all-embracing word "stress." It is indicative of conceptual shortcomings of contemporary research on exercise that the term "stress" has found acceptance also in the scientific literature on athletics. It frequently represents a dialectical ruse to hide the fact that we do not possess a system of specific identification of human movements whose autonomic accompaniments can now be recorded and measured with admirable exactitude.

The following statement was made by Sir *George Pickering*:

> Stress is an old word, but now part of the popular modes of expressing in jargonese. I am never sure what it means. The classical language of biology uses two expressions—namely 'stimulus' to describe a change in environment, and 'response' to describe the resulting change in the organism. The modern use of the word stress we owe to Selye who took it to express the first stage in the common reaction to a variety of harmful environmental changes. It was thus the first stage in the response to certain kind of stimuli. Others have used the word stress to mean a response by the mind which has been conditioned by previous experience. Others quite clearly use the word to describe environmental changes, that is stimuli. The word stress is now in common use. Whenever I meet it, I set it aside, because frankly, I do not know what it means; and I fear it is another of these words of deception. I find it difficult adequately to express my surprise and horror that contemporary science should tolerate this confusion of stimulus and response.

A scientific analysis of athletic record performances whose study is of special significance for the classification of the relationship between nutrition and physical efficiency, is not yet possible for another reason: we are unable to reproduce maximal human efforts under laboratory conditions. More relevant contributions to our understanding of athletic record performances have so far been made by coaches than by experimental scientists. The classical physiological investigations in this field by *Hill* in England and *Frucht* in Germany, both of them relying on skillful and imaginative use of statistics are exceptions which emphasize the rule. The elaboration of a system of motor notation comparable to that of staff notation in music will lead to a categorical change of the prevailing situation from which physiology and clinical medicine are equally bound to benefit.

REFERENCES

Alexander, J. K., Dennis, E. W., Smith, W. G., Amad, K. H., Duncan W. C., and Austin, R.: Blood Volume, Cardiac Output and Distribution of Systemic Blood Flow in Extreme Obesity. *Cardiovascular Research Center Bulletin,* Winter, 1962-63.

Armstrong, Donald, Dublin, L. I., Bonnet, E. C., and Marks, H. H.: *Influence of Overweight on Health and Disease.* Metropolitan Life Insurance Company, New York, 1951.

Berry, W. T. C., Beveridge, J. B., Bransby, E. R., Chalmers, A. K., Needman, B. M., Magee, H. E., Townsend, H. S., and Daubney, C. G.: The diet haemoglobin values and blood pressures of Olympic athletes. *Brit. Med. J., 1*:300, 1949.

Bramwell, M.: Diet of London busmen. *Proc. Nutr. Soc., 20*:30, 1961.

Brunner, D., and Manelis, G.: Myocardial infarction among members of communal settlements in Israel. *Lancet, 11*:1049, 1960.

Calvy, G. L., Cady, L. D., Mufson, M. A., Nierman, J., and Gertler, M. M.: Serum Lipids and Enzymes. *J.A.M.A., 183*:1, 87-90, 1963.

Christensen, E. H., and Hansen, O.: Arbeitsfähigkeit und Ernährung. III. *Skand. Arch. Physiol., 81*:160, 1939.

Curtius, F.: Konstitution. *Handbuch der inneren Medizin, VI*: 1, 1954.

Deuel, H. J., Jr., Meserve, E. R., Straub, E., Hendrick, C., and Scheer, B. T.: The effect of fat level of the diet on general nutrition. *P. Nutr., 33*:569, 1947.

Diettert, G. A.: Circulation time in the aged. *J.A.M.A., 183*:12, 1037-38, 1963.

Fletcher, W. M., and Hopkins, F. G.: Lactic acid in amphibian muscle. *J. Physiol., 35*:247, 1907.

Frucht, A. H.: *Die Grenzen der menschlichen Leistungsfähigkeit im Sport.* Akademie Verlag. Berlin, 1960.

Gertler, M. M., Driskel, M. M., Bland, E. F., Garns, S. M., Lerman, J., Levine, S. M., and White, P. D.: Clinical aspects of coronary heart disease. An analysis of 100 cases in patients 23-40 years of age with myocardial infarction. *J.A.M.A., 146*:1291, 1951.

Gertler, M. M., and White, P. D., with the aid, advice and assistance of Bland, E. F., Fertig, J., Garn, S. M., Lerman, J., Levine, S. A., Sprague, H. B., and Turner, N. C.: *Coronary Heart Disease in Young Adults.* Harvard University Press, Cambridge, 1954.

Glatzel, H.: Die Grundstoffe der Nahrung. In: *Handbuch der Allgemeinen Pathologie.* Band XI, p.l. Springer Verlag, Berlin-Göttingen-Heidelberg, 1962.

Hill, A. V.: The physiological basis of athletic records. *Lancet, 11*:481, 1925.

Hill, A. V.: *Certain Aspects of Biochemistry.* London, 1926.

Hindhede, M.: Der Eiweissbedarf des Menschen. *Munch. med. Wschr.,* 722, 1934.

Holt, L. E., Halac, J., and Kajdi, C. N.: Protein Stores and Implications in Diet. *J.A.M.A., 181*:699, 1962.

Jokl, E.: *Alter und Leistung.* Springer Verlag, Heidelberg, 1954.

Jokl, E., Karvonen, M. J., Kihlberg, J., Koskela, A., and Noro, L.: *Sports in the Cultural Pattern of the World.* Institute of Occupational Health, Helsinki, 1956.

Jokl, E.: Physical fitness and susceptibility to infections. *J. Assoc. Phys. Ment. Rehab., 13*:141, 1959.

Jokl, E.: Effects of sports and athletics on the cardiovascular system. *Encyclopedia of the Cardiovascular System,* Vol. 5. McGraw-Hill, New York, 1961.

Jokl, E.: Fitness and fatness. *J. Assoc. Phys. Ment. Rehab., 16*:2, 1962.

Karvonen, M. J. Rautanen, Y., Rikkonen, P., and Kihlberg, J.: Serum cholesterol of male and female champion skiers. *Ann. Med. Intern. Fenn., 47*:47, 1958.

Karvonen, M. J.: Effects of vigorous exercise on the heart. In: *Work and Heart,* edited by Rosenbaum, F. F., and Belknap, E. K., Paul B. Hoeber, Inc., New York, 1959.

Keller, W. D., and Kopf, H.: Unterschiede anthropologischer Masse bei vier Gruppen junger Männer mit verschiedener Aktivität. *Int. Z. angew. Physiol., 19*:110, 1961.

Keys, A.: The diet and development of coronary heart disease. *J. Chron. Dis., 4*:364, 1956.

Keys, A., and Keys, M.: *Eat Well and Stay Well.* Doubleday & Co., New York, 1959.

Keys, A.: Calories and Cholesterol. *Geriatrics,* May 1957.

Kolkka, S. (Ed.): *The Official Report of the Organizing Committee for the Games of XV Olympiad, Helsinki, 1952.* Werner Soderstrom, Helsinki, 1955.

Krogh, A., and Lindhard, J.: The relative values of fat and carbohydrates as sources of muscular energy with appendices on the correlation between standard metabolism and the respiratory quotient during rest and work. *Biochem. J., 14*:290, 1920.

Lancet Editorials: The fuel of muscular exercise, September 1959; and Protein Stores, April, 1963.

Levy, H.: Introduction to *The Notation of Movement* by Margaret Morris. Kegan, Paul, Trench, Trubner & Co., Ltd., London, 1928.

Mattill, H. I.: *Cholesterol as Related to Atherosclerosis.* A review of the literature, July 1960—July 1961. Cereal Institute, Inc., Chicago, 1962.

Mayer, J., and Bullen, B.: Nutrition and athletic performance. *Junior Swimmer, Swimming World, 3*:3, 1962.

Mellerowicz, H.: *Ergometrie.* Urban & Schwarzenberg, Munchen, 1962.

Meyerhof, O.: *Intermediate Carbohydrate Metabolism.* Symposium on respiratory enzymes. University of Wisconsin Press, Madison, 1942.

Morris, J. N.: Health and social class. *Lancet, 1*:303, 1959.

Morris, J. N., and Crawford, M. D.: Coronary heart disease and physical activity of work. *Brit. Med. J., II*: 1485, 1518, 1958.

Morris, J. N., Hardy, J. A., Raffle, P. A. B., Roberts C. G., and Parks, J. W.: Coronary heart disease and physical activity. *Lancet, II*:1053, 1953.

Nikkila, E. A., and Kontinen, A.: Effect of physical activity on post-prandial levels of fat in serum. *Lancet*, p. 1151-54, 1962.

Nothdurft, H.: Über Ernährung and motorische Aktivität. II. Mitt. Über eine spezifisch motorische Wirkung der Nahrung. *Pfluger's Arch. ges. Physiol., 242*:700, 1939.

Nothdurft, H., and Eisenbiesser, H. E.: Uber Ernährung und motorische Aktivität. III. Mitt. *Pfluger's Arch. ges. Physiol., 248*:21, 1944.

Nothdurft, H., and Eisenbiesser, H. E.: Uber Ernährung und motorische Aktivität. *Pfluger's Arch. ges. Physiol., 250*:474, 1948.

Pettenkofer, M., von, and Voit, E.: Untersuchungen uber den Stoffverbrauch des normalen Menschen. *Z. Biol., 2*:537, 1866.

Pickering, G.: Language: The lost tool of learning in medicine and science. *Lancet, II*:115, 1961.

Pomeroy, W. C., and White, P. D.: Coronary heart disease in former football players. *J.A.M.A., 167*:711, 1958.

Raab, W., and Friedmann, R.: Ernahrung and Gefassystem. *Klin. Wschr.,* 1159, 1936.

Randle, P. J., Hales, C. N., Garland, P. B., and Newsholme, E. A.: The Glucose Fatty-Acid Cycle — Its Role in Insulin Sensitivity and the Metabolic Disturbances of Diabetes Mellitus. *Lancet, 785-89,* April 1963.

Rautaharju, P. M., Karvonen, M. H., and Keys, A.: The frequency of atherosclerotic and hypertensive heart disease among ostensibly healthy working population in Finland. *J. Chron. Dis., 13*:426, 1961.

Russel, J.: *World Populations and Food Supply.* George Allen and Unwin, London, 1954.

Samuels, L. T., Gilmore, R. C., and Reinecke, R. M.: The effect of previous diet on the ability of animals to do work during subsequent fasting. *J. Nutr., 36*:639, 1948.

Schade, M., Hellebrandt, F. A., Waterland, J. C., and Carns, M. L.: Sport Reducing in Overweight College Women: Its Influence on Fat Distribution as Determined by Photography. *Research Quarterly, 33*:3, 461-71, October 1962.

Schimert, G., Schimmler, W., Schwalb, H., and Erberl, J.: Die Coronarerkrankungen. *Handbuch den Inneren Medizin,* IX, p. 653. Springer Verlag. Berlin-Göttingen, Heidelberg, 1960.

Stetten, W., and Boxer, G. E.: Studies in the carbohydrate metabolism. I. *J. Biol. Chem., 155*:231, 1944.

Taylor, H. L.: Relationship of physical activity to serum cholesterol concentration. In: *Work and the Heart.* Edited by Rosenbaum, F. F., and Belknap, E. K., Paul B. Hoeber, Inc., New York, 1959.

Wells, J. B., Parizkova, J., Jokl, E., Esser, E., Johnson, H., Bohanan, J., and Jokl, P.: Fitness and Fatness. Exercise, Excess Fat and Body Weight. The Kentucky Physical Fitness Experiment. *J. Phys. Ment. Rehab.,* Jan.-Feb., March-April, May-June, 1962.

Wertheimer, E., and Schapiro, B.: The physiology of adipose tissue. *Physiol. Rev., 28*:451, 1948.

Witkowski, M.: Analysis of methods used in physical anthropology to assess fundamental component parts of human body (in Polish). *Wychowanie fizyczne i sport,* No. 3, 1962.

Yudkin, J.: Diet and coronary thrombosis. *Lancet, II*:155, 1957.

Yudkin, J.: The causes and cure of obesity. *Lancet, II*:1135, 1959.

Chapter 2

OBESITY DUE TO PHYSICAL INACTIVITY

THE EFFECT OF INTENSIVE PHYSICAL TRAINING ON OBESE AND LEAN SUBJECTS

IN 1941, CLUVER, DE JONGH AND JOKL (2) communicated the results of a 4 months physical exercise experiment in which anthropometric measurements of previously untrained lean and obese police recruits were compared. The physical training caused lean trainees to gain and obese trainees to lose weight. Chest circumferences and bulk of muscles of the extremities increased in both groups; abdominal circumferences increased in the lean but decreased in the obese men. In other words, the nature of the morphological effects of physical training was largely determined by the amount of excess body fat. Secondly, this study was concerned with the effects of exercise regimes of different intensity. Anthropometric adjustments during training were distinctly greater in a group of men whose activity schedule was longer and more strenuous. From these observations the hypothesis was derived that *the effects of physical training upon physique are modified by the amount of excess body fat and by the intensity of the exercise regime.*

In 1945, evidence was presented showing that *physical inactivity is an essential feature of the personality of obese children* and that an intensive exercise regime causes far reaching changes of physique and character of fat boys and girls (3). In a grossly overweight boy with major developmental and behavioral abnormalities physical training caused a great loss of weight as well as the disappearance of the physical and personality disturbances originally associated with obesity. A correspondingly opposite case of an exceptionally lean boy of the same age who gained significantly under the influence of the physical training regime was shown for comparison.

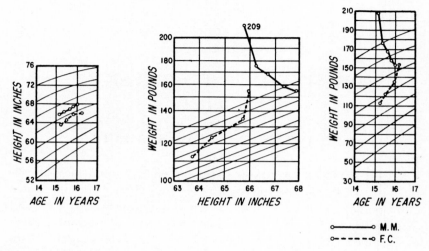

Fig. 20. Height and weight growth of an exceptionally obese and an exceptionally lean boy of 15 years of age. Both received intensive daily physical training over a period of approximately one year. The three standard grids against which the measurements are evaluated relate to height (left), height-weight (middle) and weight (right). The obese boy's starting weight was 209 pounds, his height 5 ft. 5¾ in. The lean boy's starting weight was about 100 pounds less, his height 4 ft. 11½ in. The training exerted no influence upon height but caused major changes of weight. The obese boy lost 55 pounds while the lean boy gained 43 pounds (for further explanation see text) (3).

The case under immediate reference was that of a fifteen year old youth who when first seen weighed 209 pounds; his height was 5 ft. 5-3/4 inches. The parents had been told that their child's condition was due to an "endocrine dysfunction." The boy belonged to the type which Kretschmer calls "dysplastic." He had overdeveloped breasts,* rolls of fat around abdomen, pelvis and thighs and a typical mons pubis. He was knock-kneed. He was greatly retarded in his pubertal development, belonging to stage

---

*Nydick, Bustos, Dale, Chester and Rawson (4) considered enlargement and other developmental variants of breasts during puberty such a common characteristic of obesity that in their survey on "Gynecomastia in Adolescent Boys" they excluded all adipose subjects.

II according to the standard scale of evaluation of maturity. Since stage V is normal for boys 15 years of age his maturation deficit amounted to three grades. Mentally the boy was sluggish, giving a dull and unhappy impression. His school standing was poor. He suffered from headaches. Throughout the first medical interview he sat virtually motionless. His performances in the standard physical efficiency tests were bad.

Arrangements were made for his admission to a special rehabilitation boarding school, "Physical Training Battalion"* (P.T.B.) where he received daily intensive training in calisthenics, apparatus gymnastics, weight lifting, track and field activities, games, swimming and military drill. He attended the P.T.B. for ten months. During this time three full hours per day were devoted to exercise and recreation. No dietary or specific medical measures other than the activity program were applied.

At the end of this period remarkable changes had taken place in the boy's general condition. He had lost 55 pounds of weight. He must have lost an even greater amount of fat since in accordance with the differential analysis of the body changes due to training which our subsequent studies have revealed the assumption is justified that he had gained at least 15 pounds of active body tissue. Furthermore, it is relevant to state that during the same growth period of ten months, mean weight of normal boys increases by about 12 pounds (Fig. 20). His measurement now ranged within the normal field of distribution for boys of his age.

The boy's appearance had very much improved. The visible accumulations of body fat had vanished and a distinct muscle relief was noticeable over extremities and trunk. A remarkable physiognomic reorganization had occurred to such an extent that several persons who had known the boy before his admission to the P.T.B. did not recognize him (Fig. 21). His developmental status had jumped from stage II to stage V, that is within less than a full year "compensation" had occurred for a lag of maturation amounting to an equivalent of at least four years. He was now alert, had developed initiative and felt happy in his new environment in which he was well liked. His standing in school had become distinctly above average. Physical efficiency had likewise improved, most of his performance grades ranging in

---

see: Appendix at end of chapter.

the upper quartile of the grades of his class. He played in competitive games and was a member of a successful softball team (2).

THE SIGNIFICANCE OF MOTIVATION

There is no doubt that without the exercise regime this boy would not have been able to break through the vicious circle that had caused him to be fat "because he did not move," and vice versa.

A three-fold significance attaches to this case—the first of its kind reported in the medical literature: the motivation for the initiation of the training program came from outside; no forms of treatment other than exercise were applied; and the far reaching rehabilitative adjustment that resulted from the activity regime pertained to the boy's physique and character as well as to his performance.

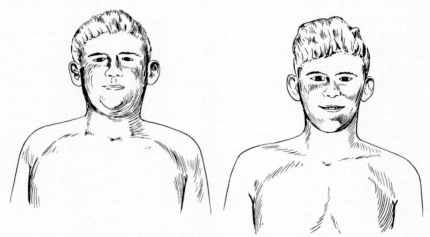

Fig. 21. Appearance of exceptionally obese 15 year old boy before and again after 10 months course of daily physical training. The drawings have been made from the original photographs in Jokl: "Effect of Training upon Obese and Lean Boys." (*S. Afr. Med. J.*, July 28, 1945). The magnitude of the morphological changes (cp. also Fig. 20) reflects corresponding changes in respect of other personality and behavioral attributes. It invites re-examination of the question in how far physique and character are determined through genetic and extraneous influences. In terms of Kretschmer's typology the fat boy was pyknic when he was admitted to the P. T. B. School but became athletic under the influence of the intensive training program.

BRUCH ON THE IMPORTANCE OF OVERWEIGHT

"It is curious that for a very long time the anatomists conspicuously ignored, or at least failed to examine the relationship between bodily composition and conformation on the one hand, and behavioral and metabolic and functional characteristics on the other. These matters, instinctively recognized as important by ordinary folks were left to the poets and to pseudo-scientists like the phrenologists" (Keys and Brozek).

In 1957, Hilde Bruch published a book entitled *The Importance of Overweight* (6) which summarizes the results of the author's studies over more than 20 years. Bruch had come to the conclusion that fat children are physically less active than lean children and that inactivity is the chief cause of obesity. The lack of exercise expresses a disturbance in these children's total approach to life, a real lack of enjoyment of physical activity due to a deep-seated mistrust about being able to master any athletic skills. Fat boys and girls save energy in every movement even though they actually use more energy than lean children if they move, because they carry a heavier body mass. Their energy saving comes in over-all economizing of every action. They do not make a single unnecessary step. Whenever possible, they will sit down and control the environment from their big chairs. *Their inhibition of activity represents a more fundamental disturbance than overeating.*

Bruch pointed out that her observations seemed to open a simple road to treatment, *viz.,* to recommend dietary restrictions and to encourage activities. However, she encountered enormous resistance when trying to put such a regime into effect. Cooperation on the part of the fat children as well as of their parents was poor.

PERSONALITY CHARACTERISTICS OF OVERWEIGHT CHILDREN

Bruch described how obese boys and girls would sit down on the only chair in the doctor's office. If the mothers were invited to sit down, they would insist on the child's sitting while they themselves remained standing. Many of the children were unable to dress themselves without aid, even those 10 years of age and older. In the case of one 14 year old boy, the mother, as a matter of routine, would go down on her knees and help him take off his shoes. Whenever a question was directed to the child, it was answered by the mother who would not let the child say one word without at least prompting or correcting him.

Another case concerned a 9 year old boy weighing 98 pounds, who was rated the most inactive child among a group of obese children. Only after repeated urgings had the parents complied with the school's request for a medical opinion. They were not concerned about the boy's fatness and actually resented the school's interference. They did not feel that either their son's extreme inactivity or his behavior were unusual.

The mother herself was the only surviving child of her mother, from whom she had never been separated. Her concept of a baby was that of a doll, and she acted like a little girl as she dressed this huge boy and stood back to admire the perfection of her work. Until age 8, the boy had made no attempt to dress himself; and even then his slowness prompted the mother to help him. He accepted such help so passively that he resembled a wooden puppet. Out of modesty he had recently protested against the mother's giving him a bath, but she had frightened him by saying that he might fall; he had acceded and promised to wait to bathe himself until he was 12 years old.

Early physical development had been normal, but there had been continuous concern about his health. When the boy was 3 years old, a tonsillectomy had been performed as a preventive measure. A mild hemorrhage occurred after the operation which led to tremendously restrictive measures. For the ensuing 6 years he was constantly reminded to walk quietly and not to play and run because otherwise he would bleed again.

The school had been concerned about his inability and disinclination to do anything for himself. He was resistant to learning self-care, although in general he was obedient and compliant. He showed a similar resistance to acquiring other physical skills which his mother had not specifically fostered. A friendly but aloof quality and a deep-seated determination not to change pervaded his whole behavior (6).

Several of the fat children were not only unable to dress themselves but had not even been trained to perform many of the ordinary tasks of self-care or to contribute to the household chores. They did not participate in games and athletics and they preferred sedentary occupations. There was always disinclination to take part in physical activities and they often showed fear of learning anything that required muscular skill or exertion. Evidently, considerable reduction of energy expenditure was caused by their passive behavior.

SPONTANEOUS WALKING ACTIVITIES OF OBESE
AND NON-OBESE WOMEN

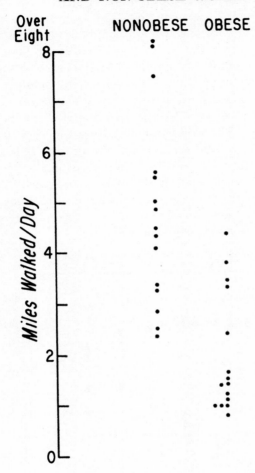

Comparison of Walking Activity of
Nonobese and Obese Women

Fig. 22. Each point represents the average daily walking distance measured for every subject with a mechanical pedometer (manufactured by the New Haven Clock Company). The mean walking distance covered by the obese women was 2.0 miles per day, as compared with 4.9 miles per day for the non-obese women. (Adapted after Chirico and Stunkard.)

The study by A. J. Stunkard *et al.* (7) used a mechanical device (pedometer) to count the number of steps taken by obese and non-obese men and women. To assess individual attitudes towards physical activity the authors applied the questionnaire and sentence completion test by R. J. Dorris *et al.* (8) and the non-parametric statistical evaluation technique of S. Siegel (9). They found that the obese subjects walked significantly less than non-obese subjects. (Obese women walked an average of 2.0 miles per day as compared with 4.9 miles per day for the non-obese controls (Fig. 22). The comparable figures for men were 3.7 and 6.0 miles.) As to the second hypothesis, viz. that physical activity has correlates in more enduring measures of behavior, the obese women's replies to questionnaires indicated that they were more passive than non-obese women in situations of despondency, boredom and social interaction. The obese men did not thus differ from non-obese controls.

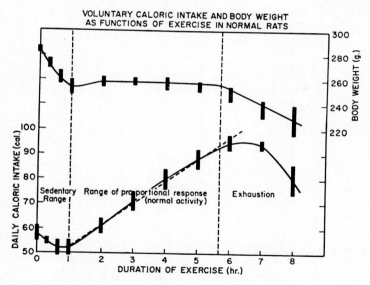

Fig. 23. "That in a normal, reasonably exercised animal or person an increase in food intake follows an increase in activity is true; it explains why the weight of most adult animals and men is relatively constant. Proper adjustments of appetite prevent the body from indefinitely burning away reserves if the individual is called upon to perform at higher levels of exertion than hitherto customary. However, experimental results show that

JEAN MAYER ON EXERCISE, NUTRITION AND WEIGHT CONTROL

Jean Mayer (10) found that obese mice were 50 to 100 times less active than non-obese animals; that inactivity precedes the development of obesity; and that the latter is not the cause of the former. Drastic reduction of weight gain during growth was brought about in genetically obese mice by treadmill exercise. Growing obese members of a strain of mice who carried the "waltzing" gene and thus were in constant rotary movement gained weight at a rate which was only about 30 per cent greater than that of non-obese mice, compared with 200-300 per cent gains shown during growth by "sedentary" obese mice. Mayer also noted that "reducing the weight of obese animals through exercise had a more lasting effect that through curtailment of food."

In an attempt to clarify the dependence of body weight and food

---

this is true only within a certain range, which has been termed by the author "normal activity range." It had been shown that rabbits when restricted in their activity by confinement in a small cage, will consume more calories than they require, and accumulate fat. The excess food consumed is characteristic of the strain; hence a hereditary factor is involved here. The same phenomenon is illustrated by the fact that rats can be made obese by total immobilization."

"When mature rats accustomed to a sedentary (caged) existence were exercised on a treadmill for increasing daily periods, it was observed that for low durations of moderate exercise (20 minutes to 1 hour) there was no corresponding increase in food intake. Actually food intake decreased slightly but significantly. Body weight also decreased. For longer durations of exercise (one to five or six hours), food intake increased linearly and weight was maintained (range of proportioned response, or normal activity range). For very long durations of exercise, the animals lost weight, their food intake decreased, and their appearance deteriorated (exhaustion range). Both the sedentary and the exhausion ranges can thus be considered "nonresponsive" ranges with respect to food intake as, in these ranges, an increase in activity is not accompanied by a corresponding increase in food intake. Of particular interest to the problem of obesity is obviously the sedentary "nonresponsive" zone. It demonstrates that under abnormal environmental conditions forcing partial immobilization or at least a sedentary life on the subject, the limits below which the regulation of food intake no longer responds by a decrease to a decrease in activity, is overtaken. Adiposity is the unavoidable result. This, of course, has been known empirically to farmers for centuries and explains the practice of cooping up or penning up cattle, hogs, and geese for fattening" (Jean Mayer) (10).

intake upon physical activity, Mayer made "sedentary" rats run the treadmill. A slight but significant decrease in food intake occured in animals who ran between 20 minutes and one hour daily. Body weight decreased at the same time. When the daily exercise sessions were extended to five or six hours, food intake rose while weight remained stationary. When exercise demands were increased to more than six hours per day, the animals became so exhausted that they no longer ate adequately and lost weight (Fig. 23). Mayer characterizes the "sedentary" and "exhaustion" ranges as "non-responsive." In these two ranges, according to the author, the relationship between energy output and energy supply is non-adaptive as shown by the fact that the "sedentary" animals gained and the over-exercised animals lost weight, while in the wide sector between these two correspondingly opposite fields of under- and over-exertion respectively, energy output and energy supply are matched.

Summary

Physical inactivity is the most significant etiological factor in obesity. Obese subjects lose excess fat if they exercise. A sustained regime of intensive physical training may completely change their physique and character. In adolescence obesity is frequently accompanied by marked delay in puberty and exercise exerts a remedial influence also upon developmental retardation. Under the influence of exercise all structural, behavioral, metabolic and functional characteristics of fat children undergo decisive changes. Extent and effectiveness of morphological maladjustments to training of obese individuals depend upon intensity of physical activity.

APPENDIX

"Physical Training Battalion" was the designation given to a remarkable social and rehabilitative experiment, undertaken more than 25 years ago at the initiative of the late General J. C. Smuts, Prime Minister of the Union of South Africa. The aim of the experiment was to take remedial action on a major educational, medical and psychological problem raised by the existence in South Africa of a large section of the population known as "Poor Whites," *viz.* economically and physically substandard persons of European descent. The historical and sociological implications of the issue had been exhaustively studied during the late twenties in a comprehensive scientific research survey sponsored by the Carnegie Corporation of New York. (*The Poor White Problem in South Africa*, Vol. I, Economic Report, Rural Impoverishment and Rural Exodus, by J. F. W. Grosskopf; Vol. II, Psychological Report, The Poor White, by R. W. Wilcocks; Vol. III, Educational Report, Education and the Poor White, by E. G. Malherbe; Part IV, Health Report, Health Factors in the Poor White Problem, by W. A. Murray; Vol. V, Sociological Report, a) The Poor White and Society, by J. R. Albertyn; b) The Mother and Daughter in the Poor White Family, by M. E. Rothmann; Stellenbosch, 1932).

A common denominator of the complex array of causes of the progressive deterioration of the status of the "Poor White" was that their work capacity was critically reduced. Most of them were unemployed because they were unemployable. Virtually all of them were physically unfit. A vicious circle had established itself in that environmental conditions had produced human misery on a large scale which in turn led to further decline.

In 1933 a special battalion was established at the Roberts Heights Military Training Center in Transvaal, for the purpose of "combating the deteriorating influence of unemployment and of providing discipline and training for unemployed boys and young men." The cost of the scheme amounted to approximately $400,000, the amount being provided by the Departments of Defense and Labor. Recruiting was confined to youths between the ages of 17 and 22. In urban areas recruiting was undertaken by the Department of Labor; in rural areas by the Department of Police. Final selection was entrusted to a board consisting of representatives of the Departments of Defense and Labor.

In the rehabilitative management of the young men a multitude of interwoven problems had to be faced, among them malnutrition, social and behavioral defects of various kinds, medical and occupational shortcomings. Many of the boys were underweight, some were excessively fat. Without exception they were unfit for labor and defense. The methods applied in their rehabilitation were basically the same as those used traditionally in the British Defense Force for purposes of pre-military training: educational, medical, disciplinary and vocational. However, special schools and vocational training centers had to be established to deal with the exceptional situation. Intensive physical exercise instruction, swimming and recreational activities formed part of the daily training program. The average length of rehabilitation was 11 months, a surprisingly short period. Between 1933 and 1939 a total of 13,825 boys were attached to the battalion. Of these 10,735 completed their training with the result that 9,409 were subsequently placed in employment (for details and a scientific analysis of the results of this scheme see monograph *Training and Efficiency, an Experiment in Physical and Economic Rehabilitation* by E. Jokl, E. H. Cluver, C. Goedvolk, and T. de Jongh, Johannesburg, South Africa, 1941, p. 188).

REFERENCES

1. Kretschmer, E.: *Korperbau and Charakter.* Berlin. Springer Verlag, 1960.
2. Cluver, E. H., de Jongh, T. W., and Jokl, E.: Some Physiological Sub-Determinators of the Reaction of the Human Organism to Physical Training—An Analysis of Measurements of 171 South African Police Recruits. *South African Journal of Science,* Vol. XXXVIII, January 1942 (paper presented in 1941.)
3. Jokl, E.: Effect of Training upon Obese and Lean Boys. *South African Med. Jnl.,* July 28, 1945.
4. Nydick, M., Bustos, J., Dale, J. H., and Rawson, R. W.: Gynecomastia in Adolescent Boys. *J.A.M.A.,* 178:5, November 4, 1961.
5. Keys, Ancel and Brozek, Josef: Body Fat in Adult Men. *Physiological Reviews, 33*:3, July 1953.
6. Bruch, Hilde: *The Importance of Overweight.* New York, Norton, 1957.
7. Stunkard, A. J. and Chirico, Anna-Marie: Physical Activity and Human Obesity. *New England Journal of Medicine, 263*:935-940, November 10, 1960.
8. Dorris, R. J., Levinson, D. J., and Hanfmann, E.: Authoritarian Personality Studied by a New Variation of the Sentence Completion Technique. *J. Abnorm. and Social Psychol., 49*:99-108, 1954.
9. Siegel, S., *Nonparametric Statistics for the Behavorial Sciences.* New York, McGraw-Hill, 1956.
10. Mayer, Jean: *Exercise and Weight Control.* (Chapter 16 in 'Science and Medicine of Exercise and Sports.' New York, Harper, 1960.)

Chapter 3

EXERCISE, EXCESS FAT
AND BODY WEIGHT

BEHNKE, FEEN AND WELHAM ON SPECIFIC GRAVITY
AND FAT CONTENT OF BODY

In 1942, BEHNKE *et al.* (2) published two important papers on
the relationship between specific gravity and fat content of the
body of healthy men, *viz,* a) "Body Weight ÷ Volume as an
Index of Obesity"; b) "Body Weight ÷ Volume and other Physical
Characteristics of Exceptional Athletes and of Naval Personnel."
In accordance with Archimedes' principle, body volume can be
determined by hydrostatic weighing whereby "equivalent volume"
is ascertained as the difference between weight in air and weight in
water. Corporeal density serves as an "index of the amount of
excess adipose tissue." The weight in water is determined by
suspending a subject below the surface of the water on a line
leading to a spring scale graduated in ounces. A weighted lead
belt maintains negative buoyancy for all types of persons. Special
methods have to be employed to measure vital capacity and
residual air.

The average weight in water of a group of 28 men whose mean
weight was 148.7 pounds and whose specific gravity was low
(1.056) amounted to 9.4 pounds. The corresponding values for
a high specific gravity group of 38 men whose mean weight was
176 pounds were 1.081 and 11.1. The difference in weight in air
between the two groups was 27.3 pounds.

On the assumption based on the above figures that a loss
of 27.3 pounds of body weight in air is associated with a gain
of weight in water of 1.7 pounds (11.1—9.4) the conclusion
was drawn that if men in the low specific gravity group would

53

have lost this amount, their specific weight would have risen from an initial value of 1.056 to 1.081; that is, for every pound of weight lost the weight of the body in water would have increased 0.062 pounds. The specific gravity of the reduced tissues was calculated as 0.94. This value is in accord with the specific gravity of adipose tissue.

Thus, the difference between the specific gravity of the two groups was attributed to a variation in adipose tissue. In explanation it was pointed out that the body may be viewed as comprising calcium salts representing 50 per cent of the weight of bone, essential or irreducible lipoid substance, excess adipose tissue and all other tissues of the body, embracing chiefly muscle, organs, brain, skin and blood. *The specific gravity of the mineral substance of bone is of the order of 3.0 adipose tissue 0.94; and all other tissue 1.060.*

In contrast with bone, the amount of excess fat is subject to wide variations and a value of 30 per cent of the total body weight is not unreasonable for obese persons. For example, if a lean man weighing 140 pounds accumulates 60 pounds of adipose tissue, the specific gravity of the body will be lowered from 1.082 to 1.035. Since the density of the mass of tissue exclusive of bone and fat may be considered constant for healthy men the *amount of fat appears to be the main factor determining specific gravity.*

CIRCUMFERENTIAL BODY MEASUREMENTS AS INDICATORS OF EXCESS SUBCUTANEOUS FATS

In Figure 24, (A) represents the volume of a lean body mass weighing 200 pounds (90.0 kg). Its specific gravity amounts to 1.082. It is divided into components 1, 2 and 3, *i.e.,* lean tissue, bone and essential fat. In (B) the inner circle encompasses a mass similar to (A) in specific gravity and composition, but differing in weight by 60 pounds (27.3 kg). The outer circle circumscribes an accumulation of 60 pounds (27.3 kg) of adipose tissue. The specific gravity of this 200 pound mass is 1.035, in contrast with the value of 1.082 for the mass represented by the inner circle. To reiterate: percentage variations of specific gravity of lean tissue and bone are small and for all practical purposes constant;

excess fat is the prime factor governing the level of specific gravity.

Behnke and co-workers drew attention to the fact that diet and exercise exert a major effect upon specific gravity. A man placed on a restricted diet and engaging in systematic exercise lost 19.5 pounds over a period of 7 months. His net weight in water increased from 10.8 pounds to 12.1 pounds although the corresponding weight in air decreased from 202.5 pounds to 183.0 pounds. Thus for every pound of weight lost in air, the weight in water increased 0.067 pound (1.3 ÷ 19.5). The specific gravity of the reduced tissue is, therefore, computed to be 0.937 (1.000 ÷ 1.067). Again, this value is in accord with the specific gravity of neutral fat.

In 99 healthy young men specific gravity tended to increase inversely in relation to body weight; the difference between abdominal and thoracic girth correlated with specific gravity. In lean subjects this difference is greater than it is in fat subjects. That in obese individuals abdominal girth decreases during training

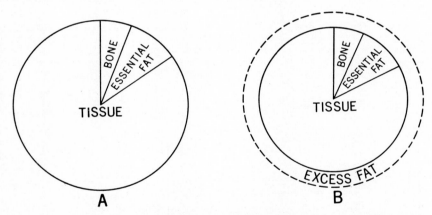

Fig. 24. (A) represents the volume of a lean body mass weighing 200 pounds (90.0 kg). Its specific gravity amounts to 1.082. It is divided into components 1, 2, and 3, *i.e.*, lean tissue, bone and essential fat. In (B) the inner circle encompasses a mass similar to (A) in specific gravity and composition but differing in weight by 60 pounds (27.3 kg). The outer circle circumscribes an accumulation of 60 pounds (27.3 kg) of adipose tissue. The specific gravity of this 200 pounds mass is 1.035, in contrast with the value of 1.082 for the mass represented by the inner circle.
(Behnke et al.)[2]

had been demonstrated in 1941 by Cluver, de Jongh and Jokl (3) who suggested that the eliminated tissue was fat. All circumferential measurements taken before and after a prolonged period of intensive physical training from body regions where excess fat is deposited may reflect the phenomenon under reference (Fig. 25). Jokl *et al.* (4) found a statistically significant tendency towards decrease of hip circumferences in a group of adolescent high school girls who had exercised daily for 4-1/2 months; while an opposite trend was manifest in an active control group.

If obesity and not weight *per se* is the chief factor tending to produce low values for specific gravity, heavy but lean men should possess a high average value for specific gravity. In order to test this thesis Behnke *et al.* studied 25 "All-American" football players

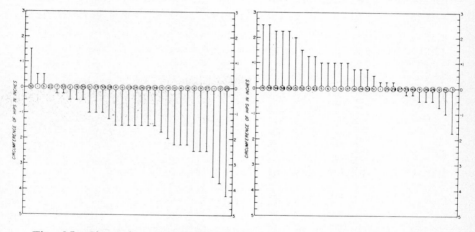

Fig. 25. Circumferential Hip Measurements in Trained and Untrained Adolescent Girls. All circumferential measurements taken from body regions where excess fat is deposited reflect the effect of intensive physical training. The validity of this statement is shown by this diagram in which differences in the circumference of hips before and after a 4½ months period of daily intensive physical training as ascertained in a group of 34 adolescent girls are plotted (left). For purposes of comparison corresponding measurements from a control group are presented (right), which show a statistically significant tendency towards increases of circumferences of hips due to normal growth. The opposite tendency in the diagram on the left expresses the magnitude of effectiveness of intensive physical training.

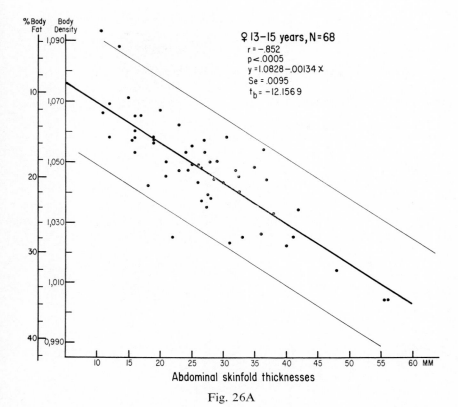

♀ 13−15 years, N=68
r = −.852
p < .0005
y = 1.0828 − .00134 X
Se = .0095
t_b = −12.1569

Abdominal skinfold thicknesses

Fig. 26A

Fig. 26 A & B. Abdominal (A) and sum of ten skinfold thicknesses (B) of 68 girls, 13-16 years of age, are correlated with body density according to the following logarithmic regression curve:

1. $y = 1.205 - 0.078 \log x$

where y is body density and x is the sum of the 10 skinfolds. The correlation coefficient is $r = -0.833$, the standard error of estimate 0.032 (a). Abdominal skinfold thickness plays a dominant role in that it represents a very large part of excess fat deposits; and in that its modifications with physical activity and inactivity, respectively, parallel the changes under reference in their entirety. Keys and Brozek's formula was applied whereby

2.   Per cent of body fat = $\dfrac{420.1}{\text{body density}} - 381.3$.

An excellent linear—not a logarithmic—relationship was obtained between these two measurements, namely

3. $y = 1.0828 - (.00134) x$

The correlation coefficient is $r = -0.852$, the standard error of estimate

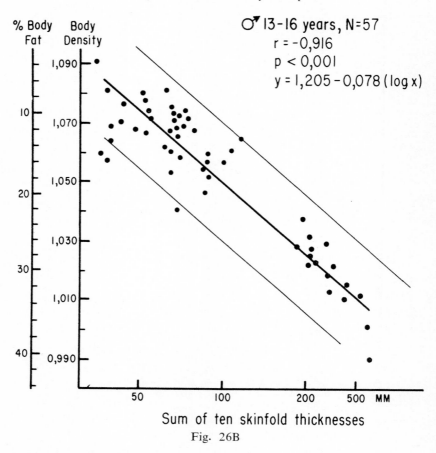

Sum of ten skinfold thicknesses

Fig. 26B

.0095. Assuming that the errors of estimate are normally distributed with mean zero and standard deviation one, the probability of obtaining this linear model by chance is less than .0005.

The relationship (3) was then used to compute body density and excess fat; bone and essential fat being assumed to be 20 per cent of the total body weight, in accordance with the data presented by Behnke *et al.* Active body tissue was determined from

4.   (Body Weight) — (Excess Fat) — (Body and Essential Fat).

*The following values were obtained on the 25 exceptional athletes: The averages listed in whole number yielded values for specific gravity of 1.080, for weight cf 200 pounds (90 kg), for height of 72 inches (182.9 cm), for age of 25 years, for circumference of chest of 40 inches (101.6 cm) and for abdomen of 33 inches (83.8 cm). These findings once more corroborated the validity of the conclusion that adipose tissue and not weight per se is the governing factor determining specific gravity.

whose average weight was 200 pounds (90.0 kg), with an average specific gravity of 1.080.* According to current standard heavyweight tables most of these men "could be classified as unfit for military service and as not qualified as risks for first class insurance by reason of overweight."

The study by Behnke *et al.* showed that standard tables merely interpret weight in relation to height while specific gravity or *weight of tissue per unit volume* gives a true "index of proper weight."

ANCEL KEYS AND JOSEF BROZEK'S MONOGRAPH

In 1953, there appeared in the *Physiological Reviews,* Ancel Keys and Josef Brozek's monograph, *Body Fat in Adult Men* (5), an admirable work which marked the beginning of a new era of research in the field under reference.

The authors stressed the usefulness of skinfold calipers for the

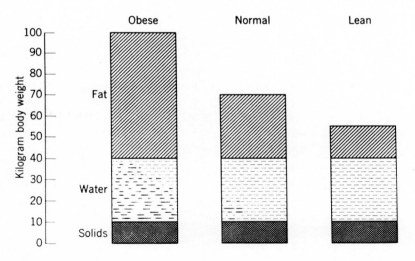

Fig. 27. "Lean tissue" comprises 73 per cent of body water. Two-thirds of these 73 per cent are intracellular. The remainder is extracellular. The body, however, consists also of the skeleton and of fat deposits. Water content of extracellular fluid and skeleton are virtually constant. However, fat deposits (adipose tissue) contain relatively little water, so that obese individuals have a relatively smaller water content than lean persons. Variations of fat are the main source of variations in total body water among individuals. [After Rogers (6).]

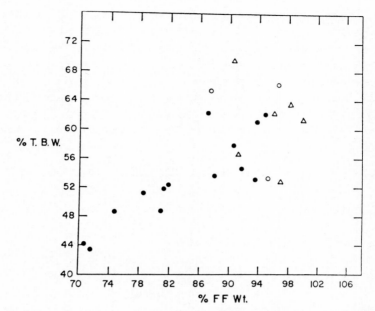

Fig 28. The variation in per cent of total body water (% TBW) and per cent of fat-free body weight (% FFWt) in three groups of students varying in physical activity habitus. (Buskirk,)
● Sedentary   O Intramural participants   ▲ Varsity athletes

determination of subcutaneous fat but observed that no unanimity had been reached at the time as to the choice of sites, techniques of measurement and methods of evaluation. Also skinfold calipers had not yet been standardized.**

Of great importance was the discovery by Keys and Brozek of a good correlation between specific gravity and skinfold measure-

---

**The problem of standardization of skinfold calipers has received detailed consideration at the University of Kentucky by K. Lange who designed an excellent instrument (produced by the Cambridge Scientific Industries, Inc., 18 Poplar Street, Cambridge, Maryland) with
1. Pivoted tips which adjust automatically for parallel measurements of skinfolds—rectangular faces with well-rounded edges and corners for patient comfort—face area is approximately 30 mm.²
2. An easy-to-read scale which permits reading up to 60 mm accurate to ± 0.5 per cent of full scale.
3. Spring loaded levers which provide a substantially constant standard pressure of 10 gm/mm² over the entire operating range—all critical pivot points utilize low friction bearings to maintain accurate tip pressure at all jaw openings.

ments. Thus, ready appraisal was made possible of relative and excess fatness in human subjects. The authors pointed out that for many research purposes as well as practical applications absolute accuracy is not essential, and it is not even important to know the total amount of fat in the body. It is enough, according to the authors, to know the difference in fat between two bodies or the difference in the same person at different times. As a rule actual values of the skinfolds can be used as criteria of fatness.

Keys and Brozek established the first equations for predicting body fat on the basis of single skinfolds and of different combinations of skinfolds. The intercorrelations between skinfolds were found to be rather high (0.752-0.938). The region of diminishing (and vanishing) returns in adding skinfolds beyond three or four well-selected and optimally weighed sites is rapidly reached. Thus, while generally multiple skinfold measurements are preferable, estimates derived from single skinfold measurements may reliably

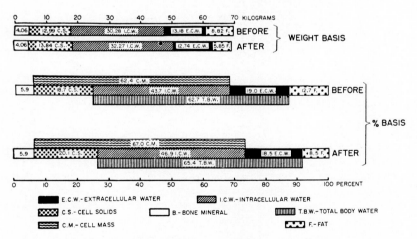

Fig 29A. Body Composition of Soldiers Before and After Paratrooper Training. Paratrooper Training was of Three Weeks' Duration.

Pascale *et al.* measured extra-cellular fluid and total body water in 12 men before and after a 3 weeks paratrooper training course. Various body composition analyses were undertaken in this study. Extra cellular fluid did not change. Total body water increased; body fat decreased. Methods: ECW: radiosulphate space; TBW: deuterium oxide space; ICW: TBW — ECW; CM: = ICW/0.7; CS: = 0.3 CM; B: = 0.134 ICW; F: = estimated from body fluids (After Buskirk).

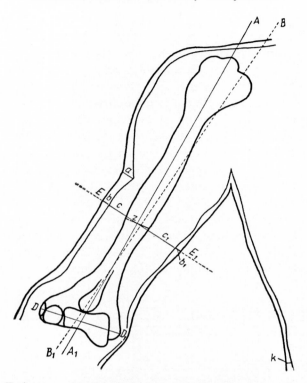

Fig. 29B. Estimates of subcutaneous fat depots can be made roentgeno-logically. One of the best studies using X-Ray techniques for the assess-ment of excess body fat has been conducted at the 'Polish Institute for Research in Physical Culture' under the direction of Prof. W. Missiuro in Warsaw by M. Witkowski from whose paper the above diagram has been taken. Space diameters identified as a, b, bl and k vary in accordance with amounts of fat deposited subcutaneously. This method was used by J. M. Tanner in his study conducted in Rome in 1960 "The Physique of the Olympic Athlete" (monograph, Allen & Unwin, London, 1964).

reflect total trends, and have been used in longitudinal studies. The validity of the underlying methodological assumption is born out by the correlation diagrams in Figure 26A and 26B.

BODY WATER AND BODY FAT

A different methodological approach to the problem under reference is based upon the fact that the water content of the body varies in accordance with its fat. Adipose tissue contains little water so that obese persons have a relatively smaller water content than lean persons. The density of fat is about 0.90 at 37° C and that of "cells" approximately 1.057. Thus, the denser subject will have a proportionately greater fat-free body weight than his less dense, obese counterpart. Fat contains 20-30 per cent water while lean tissue contains 65-75 per cent. Figure 27 (6) shows that subjects with the same mass of "solids" and of water may greatly differ in weight solely as a result of varying amounts of fat. From Figure 28 it can be seen that percentage values of body water are much greater in untrained individuals than in athletes. Pascale *et al.* (7) who determined body water and computed adipose tissue

Fig. 30A. Standardized skinfold caliper designed at the University of Kentucky by Dr. Karl Lange.

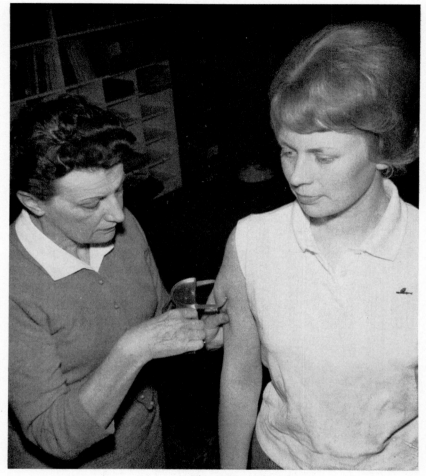

Fig. 30B

from their data also found a decrease of body fat with training (Fig. 29). Buskirk (8) has summarized our present knowledge of the problem in a paper, "Exercise and Body Fluid." It must of course be realized that analyses of body fluids do not allow a differentiation between "essential" and "excess" fat. Since it is the latter which is primarily and perhaps exclusively modified by exercise the relevance of studies of body fluids for the clarification of the relationship between fitness and fatness is somewhat limited.

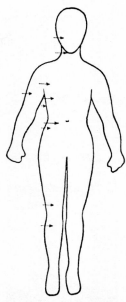

Fig. 31. Arrows point at standard skinfold locations used in study.

PARIZKOVA'S STUDIES (9)

In 1956, Allen *et al.* (1) corroborated Keys and Brozek's con-clusions and established a direct correlation between specific gravity and combined skinfold measurements taken at cheek, chin, thorax (2 places), upper arm, back, abdomen, hip, thigh and calf. Parizkova extended these studies by establishing norms of sub-cutaneous fat layers at ten places for normal and obese boys and girls between seven and 16 years of age thus obtaining concise in-formation also on what she subsequently called the development during puberty of a "sexual bimorphism" in the distribution of subcutaneous fat in boys and girls (Fig. 32).

Against the background of such and other data quantitative studies could be undertaken of the effect of physical training on body fat (Figs. 32-34).

An investigation which extended over 30 months was concerned with the effect of different intensities of physical training upon skinfold thicknesses of girls, ages 14 and 15. The upper section of Figure 33 shows combined skinfold measurements, the middle section skinfold profile changes, the bottom section modifications

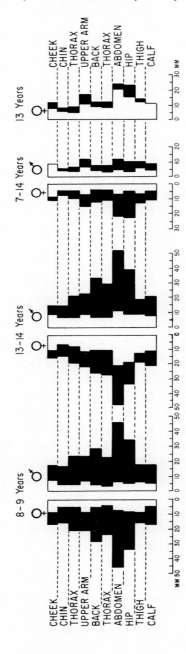

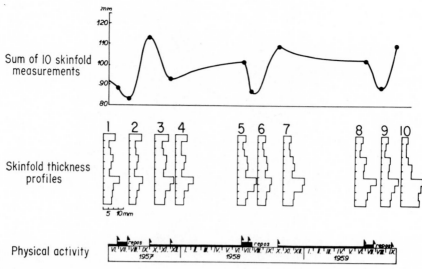

Sum of 10 skinfold measurements

Skinfold thickness profiles

Physical activity

Fig. 33. Fluctuations of Excess Fat Under the Influence of Different Exercise Regimes in Girls Age 14 and 15 Over a Period of 30 Months. The upper section shows compound changes of 10 skinfold measurements, the middle section corresponding skinfold thickness profiles, the bottom section modifications of physical training during the study. Physical inactivity ("repos") caused fat to be deposited subcutaneously while resumption of training led to a reduction which was greatest with the most intensive exercise regimes. Between 1 and 2, 5 and 6, and 8 and 9 intensity of training was maximal. Between 2 and 3, 6 and 7, and 9 and 10 training was suspended. Between 4 and 5, and 7 and 8 training was maintained but on an intensity level less than that of the 'maximal' periods.

Fig. 32. Profile Diagrams of Skinfold Thicknesses. The first two profiles (A) represent skinfold measurement from normal and obese boys and girls of 8 to 9 years of age. The unshaded portions refer to measurements from lean; the white and black portions combined to measurement from obese children. The black portions identify the amount of surplus fat in the latter. The second two profiles (B) represent the same measurements as those referred to for (A), from normal and obese boys and girls of 13 and 14 years of age. The third two profiles (C) illustrate developmental changes in subcutaneous fat distribution in non-obese boys and girls between 7 and 14 years of age. The appearance in non-obese children at puberty of a "sexual bimorphism" is evident. By contrast the measurements of obese boys and girls continue to remain virtually identical as a comparison of profile outlines (B) reveals. That is, no sexual differences are found in respect of excessive fat content in obese children such as are usual for normal children. Column (D) represents skinfold measurements for trained (unshaded portion) and untrained (shaded plus black portion) girls of 13 years of age. The trained children had less fat than the untrained ones.

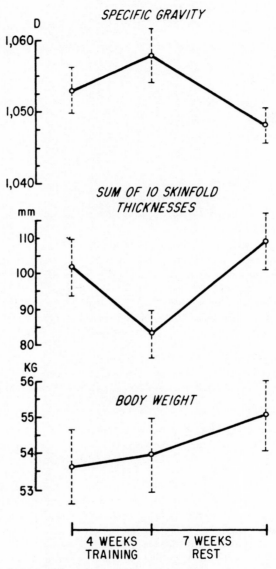

Fig 34A. Effect of Training Upon Specific Gravity, Excess Fat and Body Weight. After 4 weeks of intensive physical training adolescent girls showed an increase of specific gravity and body weight and a decrease of excess fat. Following a 7 weeks period of inactivity, specific gravity decreased while excess fat increased and body weight rose above the post-training level.

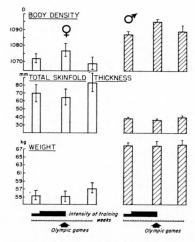

Fig. 34B. Body composition of Czechoslovakian national gymnastic teams (men and women) before and after their competitions at the Olympic Games in Rome in 1960. Body density, total skinfold thickness and body weight indicated an extremely favorable state of training of the champion gymnasts several months before the contests. However, this highly selected group of athletes continued to improve during the maximally intensified exercise period immediately prior to the Games in that their body density increased, skinfold thicknesses regressed and technical proficiency improved still further. Contrariwise, during the weeks following the competitions a reverse trend was in evidence: body density decreased, skinfold thicknesses increased and weight went up.

of the physical training regime. Physical inactivity ("repos") caused fat to be rapidly deposited while resumption of training promptly led to a reduction which was greatest when the exercise regime was intensified (thick horizontal black lines).

Figure 34A which relates to another study compares specific gravity, subcutaneous fat deposits and body weight of girls before and after a 4 weeks intensive physical training period. Marked increase of specific gravity, a decrease of excess fat and a slight increase of body weight are in evidence. Following a 7-week period of inactivity there occurred a decrease in specific gravity, accompanied by an increase of fat deposits and by a significant gain in body weight* (See also Fig. 34B).

*The following observation is recorded by Stunkard and Chirico (10): Eight obese men had served in the armed forces and had undergone the discipline of the basic-training period. Of these 8 men, 6 reported that they had lost from 4.5 to 13.6 kg. (10 to 30 pounds) during their military service. In every case, however, the amount of weight lost was regained after cessation of training.

Summary

Body weight measurements give no indication of tissue composition. Specific gravity or weight of tissue per unit volume provides a true index of proper weight, that is of lean tissue and excess fat. A group of All-American football players weighing 200 pounds on the average would according to current standard height and weight tables have been considered unfit for military service and for first class insurance. The erroneousness of such an assumption was shown by the fact that these men had a conspicuously high specific gravity (2). To Keys and Brozek (5) goes the credit of having demonstrated a correlation between specific gravity and skinfold measurements, and thus of laying the foundation for the ready appraisal of relative and excess fatness in human subjects.

This chapter reviews data derived from the establishment of norms of subcutaneous fat layers at 10 places for children of between 7-16 years of age and presents evidence to the effect that intensive physical training causes a depletion of excess fat and an increase of specific gravity; and that inactivity has the reverse effect (9). The nature of the statistical relationship between skinfold measurements and specific gravity is detailed and an account presented of the theoretical bases for the computation thus rendered possible, of excess fat and lean tissue.

REFERENCES

1. Allen, T. H., Peng, M. T., Chen, K. P., Huang, T. F., Chang, C. W., and Fang, H. S., Prediction of Total Adiposity from Skinfolds and the Curvilinear Relationship Between External and Internal Adiposity. *Metabolism,* V. 3, May 1956.
2. Behnke, A. R., Feen, B. G., and Welham, W. C.: The Specific Gravity of Healthy Men, I+ II *J.A.M.A., 118.*7, Feb. 14, 1942.
3. Cluver, E. H., de Jongh, T. W., and Jokl, E.: Some Physiological Sub-Determinators of the Reaction of the Human Organism to Physical Training—An Analysis of Measurements of 171 South African Police Recruits. *South African Journal of Science,* Vol. XXXVIII, January 1942 (paper presented in 1941).
4. The Kentucky Physical Fitness Experiment (a) Simon, E.: Problems of Morphological and Functional Development in Physical Education, in *Health and Fitness in the Modern World.* (Symposium at Rome, Olympic Games 1960). Athletic Institute, Chicago, 1961; (b) Jokl, E.: Youth Fitness. *Amateur Athlete* 11, Nov. 1959; (c)

Gunkler, O.: The Kentucky Physical Fitness Experiment. Doctoral Thesis, University of Kentucky, 1960; (d) Physical Fitness and Susceptibility to Infections (With Reference to Observations During the Influenza Epidemic in March 1959), *Jnl. Assn. for Phys. and Ment. Rehab., 13*:5, 141-144, Sept.-Oct. 1959.

5. Keys, Ancel and Brozek, Josef: Body fat in adult men. *Physiological Reviews, 33*:3, July 1953.

6. Rogers, Terence A., *Elementary Human Physiology*. New York, John Wiley & Sons, 1961.

7. Pascale, L. R., Frankel, T., Grossman, M. I., Freeman, S., Faller, I. L., and Bond E. E.: Report of Changes in Body Composition of Soldiers During Paratrooper Training. *Army Medical Nutrition Lab. Report,* 156, 1955.

8. Buskirk, E. R. and Moore, R.: Exercise and Body Fluids. In Warren R. Johnson, *Science and Medicine of Exercise and Sports*. New York, Harper & Brothers, 1960.

9. Parizkova, J., The Development of Subcutaneous Fat in Normal and Obese Children; and the Effect of Physical Training and Sport. *Physiologia Bohemoslovenica, 8.2.* 1959. 112-17; and *9.6* 1960. 516-23. Age Trends in Normal and Obese Children. *Journal of Applied Physiology, 16*:1, 173-74, 1961.

10. Stunkard, A. J. and Chirico, Anna-Marie: Physical Activity and Human Obesity. *New England Journal of Medicine, 263*:935-940, November 10, 1960.

Chapter 4

THE KENTUCKY PHYSICAL FITNESS EXPERIMENT

THE KENTUCKY PHYSICAL FITNESS EXPERIMENT

Reduction of excess fat, one of several morphological long-term adjustments to intensive physical training is invariably accompanied by gain of lean tissue. Studies of body weight therefore do not provide information on these correspondingly opposite phenomena.

On the basis of the theoretical and statistical evidence that has been discussed in two preceding chapters, the Kentucky Physical Fitness Experiment was designed to allow separate estimates of the effect of training on 1) body weight; 2) lean tissue; and 3) excess fat. Thirty-four adolescent high school girls received daily training for 5 months; while another group of 34 girls served as controls. The first group will henceforth be called "experimental," the second, "control." The exercise curriculum consisted of calisthenics, apparatus gymnastics, weight lifting, dancing, games, track and field activities and swimming. Each teaching period was set out in such a way as to allow graphic documentation of its didactic content.

The anthropometric studies described in this chapter formed part of a multi-disciplined investigation that included also physiological, clinical, psychological and physical performance measurements.

Statistical Considerations

Various hypotheses were tested concerning the means obtained for the two groups. The assumption was made that weight, active body tissue and excess fat are each normally distributed, and that the two groups of 34 girls are independent random samples from normal populations with equal popula-

72

tion variances. The F test was used to confirm the validity of the latter supposition. Student's t-test at the 0.05 level of significance was applied throughout with the value of t being computed from the formula

1. $t = \dfrac{M_2 - M_1}{\sqrt{(n_1-1)\, s_1^2 + (n_2-1)s_2^2}} \sqrt{\dfrac{n_1 n_2 (n_1 + n_2 - 2)}{n_1 + n_2}}$

M_1 and M_2 are the means of the two groups; s_1^2 and s_2^2 the corresponding variances; and n_1 and n_2 the corresponding sample sizes. The number of degrees of freedom is $n_1 + n_2 - 2$.

In testing hypotheses about the means within a group, independent samples could be assumed. The observation had therefore to be paired. Since the population variances were assumed equal, pairings were made by subtracting individual values at the beginning of the experiment from corresponding values at the time of its conclusion. Again, differences were tested at the 0.05 level of significance. The value of t was computed from the formula:

2. $t = (D \sqrt{n})\, /s_D$

where D is the mean gain for the group, n the sample size and s_D the standard deviation. The number of degrees of freedom is $n-1$.

The hypothesis examined and the results obtained with the analysis of changes of measurements during the 5 months of the study are given in Table 1. t was computed in such a manner that its value is always positive. H_0 stands for the null hypothesis, H_1 for the alternative hypothesis. M_1^* stands for the mean gains of the experimental group and M_2^* for mean gains of the control group. The following is a summary of the findings:

1. Body weight changes after the 5 months' study showed no statistical difference between experimental and control groups.

2. During the 5 months' study, the experimental group gained an average of 4.10 pounds of active body tissue while the control group lost an average of 0.24 pounds. The difference is of high statistical significance.

3. Initial excess body fat measurements of the two groups were not significantly different, but a highly significant difference was present after the 5 months; a highly significant loss

TABLE I

			BODY WEIGHT		ACTIVE TISSUE		EXCESS FAT	
TESTS OF HYPOTHESES ON								
Hypothesis tested		d.o.f.	t	p	t	p	t	p
GROUPS OF 34 GIRLS (Totals) H_0 : M_1 = M_2 / H_1 : M_1 ≠ M_2		66	0.59	>.5	1.03	>.3	0.16	>.08
H_0 : M_1^* = M_2^* / H_1 : M_1^* < M_2^*		66	1.38	>.05	5.27	<.0005	8.48	<.0005
H_0 : M_1^* = O / H_1 : M_1^* < O		33	0.68	>.2	7.33	<.0005	10.85	<.0005
H_0 : M_2^* = O / H_1 : M_2 > O		33	1.31	>.1	0.40	>.3	2.03	<.05
11 HEAVIEST GIRLS H_0 : M_1 = M_2 / H_1 : M_1 ≠ M_2		20	1.35	>.1	1.08	>.2	1.25	>.2
H_0 : M_1^* = M_2^* / H_1 : M_1^* < M_2^*		20	2.14	<.05	1.72	<.05	4.90	<.0005
H_0 : M_1^* = O / H_1 : M_1^* < O		10	4.10	<.005	2.43	<.025	7.17	<.0005
H_0 : M_2^* = O / H_1 : M_2^* > O		10	0.15	>.4	0.63	>.25	1.18	>.1
11 LIGHTEST GIRLS H_0 : M_1 = M_2 / H_1 : M_1 ≠ M_2		20	0.94	>.3	1.31	>.1	.04	>.9
H_0 : M_1^* = M_2^* / H_1 : M_1^* > M_2^*		20	1.82	<.05	5.21	<.0005	5.97	<.0005
H_0 : M_1^* = O / H_1 : M_1^* > O		10	2.85	<.005	5.73	<.0005	6.81	<.0005
H_0 : M_2^* = O / H_1 : M_2^* > O		10	0.92	>.15	0.23	>.4	1.13	>.1

* Degree of freedom

of excess fat had occurred in the experimental group while the control group showed but a very small loss of fat.

Regression analyses were made between the various initial measurements, and gains or losses during the training. The following results were obtained:

1. A significant correlation ($r = -.54$; $t = -3.55$) was found in that in the experimental group the *lightest* girls *gained* weight while the *heaviest* girls *lost* weight during training. No such correlation was established for the measurements of the control group.

2. A significant correlation ($r = -.808$; $t = -7.76$) w a s

found in that all the girls in the experimental group lost excess fat during the training. The trend was for the girls with the highest initial excess body fat values to lose most excess fat. No such correlation was established from the measurements of the control group.

Subanalysis of "Heaviest," "Middle," and "Lightest" Group Data

Because of these findings a subanalysis was undertaken in which the two groups were divided into three sub-groups consisting of the 11 heaviest, and the 11 lightest, and a "middle group" of twelve girls. Formulas 1 and 2 were again used to test various hypotheses at the 0.05 level of significance. (Cp. Table 1)

The following is a summary of the conclusions:

Weight

1. There was no significant difference in the initial mean weights of the two groups of 34 girls and in the mean gain of weight between the two groups during the study. There was no significant mean loss of weight of the control group during the study.

2. There was no significant difference in the mean initial weights of the two groups of the 11 heaviest girls. At the end of the study, the 11 heaviest girls of the experimental group showed a significant loss, while the 11 heaviest girls in the control group had gained weight.

3. There was no significant difference in the mean initial weights of the two groups of the 11 lightest girls. The 11 lightest girls in the experimental group gained significantly in weight while the 11 lightest girls in the control group showed no significant change.

Active Body Tissue

1. There was no significant difference in the mean initial active body tissue measurements of the two groups. At the end of the study the experimental group showed a significant mean gain of active tissue while there was no significant change in the control group.

2. There was no significant difference in the mean initial active body tissue measurements of the 11 heaviest girls in the two groups. At the end of the study the 11 heaviest girls in the experimental group had gained significantly in active body tissue while the 11 heaviest girls in the control group had lost active body tissue.

3. There was no significant difference in the mean initial active body tissue measurements of the two groups of 11 lightest girls. At the end of the study the 11 lightest girls in the experimental group had gained significantly in active body tissue while the control group showed no significant change.

Excess Fat

1. There was no significant difference in mean initial body fat measurements of the two groups. At the end of the study the experimental group had lost significantly in mean excess body fat while the control group had gained significantly in excess body fat.

2. There was no significant difference between the mean initial excess body fat measurements of the 11 heaviest girls in the two groups. At the end of the study, the 11 heaviest

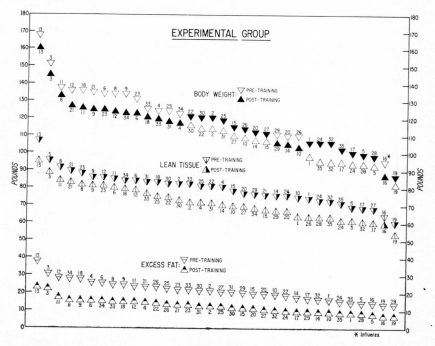

Fig. 35 A and B. Data on body weight, lean tissue and excess fat obtained before and after 5-months-study from experimental and control group, plotted in sequential order. Note that ranges of individual differences of all three factors transcend by far those of relevant growth progression means for the morphological components under study.

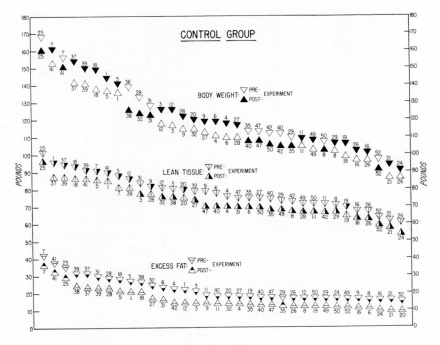

Fig. 35B

girls in the experimental group had lost significantly in excess fat; while the 11 heaviest girls in the control group showed no significant change.

3. There was no significant difference in the mean initial excess body fat measurements of the 11 lightest girls in the two groups. At the end of the study, the 11 lightest girls in the experimental group showed a significant loss in mean excess body fat while the 11 lightest girls in the control group showed no significant change.

COMMENT

To reiterate, the Kentucky Physical Fitness Experiment has shown that training causes a profound shift of body composition, *viz.* a proportional and absolute increase of lean tissue and a correspondingly opposite response of excess fat. This effect establishes itself not only in obese but also in lean children, irrespective of considerable differences in the children's diet.

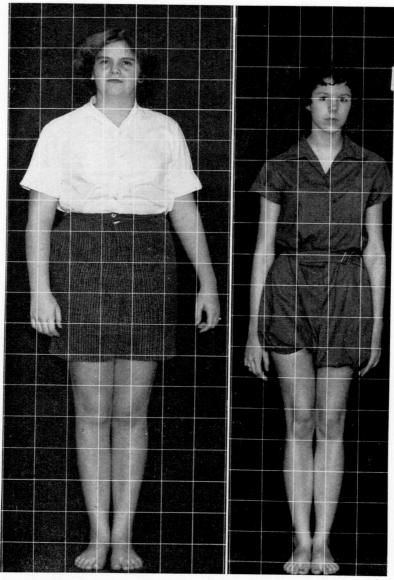

Fig. 36. The influence of physical training upon physique is small compared with the range of genetically determined variants of body measurements in normal children. The above two 15 year old girls participated

Although the results of the anthropometric analysis of physical measurements taken in our study corroborate the validity of the present medical concept of the overall dominance of hereditary over environmental determinants of body form, the very fact that physical training causes tissue changes of the magnitude indicated by our findings is of considerable importance. *Fatness represents the most ubiquitous morphological indicator of unfitness.* How well the growing concern in the United States over the widespread "softness"—to use President Kennedy's expression—among the nation's youth is justified is apparent from a recent comment by B. D. Karpinos of the Office of the Surgeon General of the Armed Forces on the causes of rejection of recruits for military service:

> The disqualification for anthropometric reasons are now by far more prominent than they have been in the past . . . They rank, at the present, fifth among the medical disqualifications while they ranked eleventh in the Korean War (1950-53). *This category gained prominence because of an increase in the number of youths disqualified for overweight.*

That this cause of "unfitness" is readily remediable has been conclusively shown by our study. It is hoped that the military authorities will draw the necessary conclusions and apply them in practice. Fatness is closely related to performance. This statement will be elaborated in subsequent references to the correlation between the body tissue changes under discussion and the results of physical efficiency tests that were conducted with the children.

The relationship between fatness and fitness is of a universal character though quantitatively its significance is of different relevance in different physical performance sectors. For example, fatness is a great handicap in long-distance running but not necessarily so in weight lifting. Under exceptional circumstances fatness may represent an advantage even in well trained performers, *e.g.*, in channel swimmers, or in paratroopers operating in Arctic terri-

---

in the Kentucky Physical Fitness Experiment: height: 63.25 and 62.50 inches; weight: 149.50 and 84 pounds; excess fat quotients: 35 and 9; lean tissue: 97 and 55 pounds. Differences in physical measurements of this magnitude in children of equal age reflect the dominant influence of heredity upon growth. (For nature and scope of modification of anthropometric components through training cp. Figs. 37 and 38.)

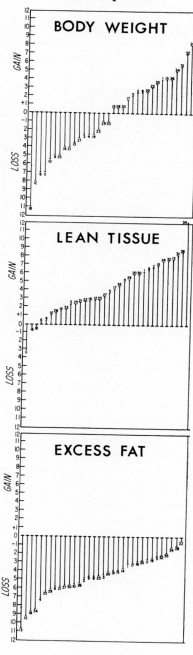

tory where special thermoregulatory requirements have to be taken into account.

Our findings have far-reaching clinical implications, *e.g.*, in cardiology where the role of body fat and blood lipids in the etiology of degenerative systemic diseases currently receives much attention. However, the respective relevance of diet and exercise has not yet been sufficiently studied in this context. The likelihood of exercise being of greater prophylactic significance than diet has recently been stressed by Brunner (1, 2, 3). This experienced investigator found that the conspicuously favorable cardiovascular morbidity and mortality situation among Yemenite Jews in their former native environment underwent a change for the worse after they immigrated into Isreal and adopted a Western type diet which is generally known to facilitate establishment and rate of progress of degenerative changes in heart and blood vessels, as Ancel Keys (4, 5, 6, 7) has shown. However, Brunner also presented evidence to the effect that a Western type diet cannot be the sole cause of the pathological trends under reference; the cardiovascular morbidity and mortality pattern of Yemenite agricultural laborers in Israel was significantly superior to that of persons in the same community who led a sedentary life. All of them consumed a Western type diet. It is quite possible that the modifications of fat and muscle metabolism through physical activity represent the physiological mediator for the cardiovascular adjustments whose pathological relevance has already been demonstrated..

Summary

A quantitative estimate has been presented in this study of the correspondingly opposite influence of physical training upon lean tissue and excess fat in adolescent girls. The methodological, statistical and theoretical considerations upon which this investigation is based have been described.

←──⟨⟨⟨⟨

Fig. 37. Differential analyses of pre- and post-study measurements of body weight, lean tissue and excess fat.

Units in pounds

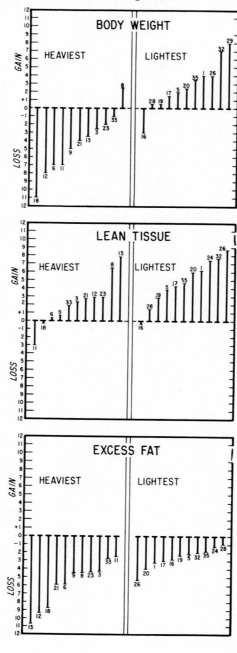

REFERENCES

1. Brunner, Daniel: Influence of Age and Race on Lipid Levels in Israel. *The Lancet,* May 23, 1959.
2. Brunner, Daniel: Ethnological Study of the Age Trend of Serum Lipids. *Israel Medical Journal,* XVII: 7-8, 1958.
3. Brunner, Daniel: Research Report in print. *A.M.A. Arch., Int. Med.,* 1964.
4. Keys, Ancel: Weight Gain from Simple Overeating. *Metabolism, IV*:5, September 1955.
5. Keys, Ancel: Body Composition and Its Change With Age and Diet. *Weight Control,* a publication of the Weight Control Colloquium, February 1955. Iowa State College. Ames, Iowa.
6. Keys, Ancel: Coronary Artery Disease. *J. Chron. Dis.,* 6:552, November 1958.
7. Keys, Ancel: Diet and Health. *Time,* January 13, 1961.

Fig. 38. Differential subanalyses of pre- and post-study measurements of body weight, lean tissue and excess fat, separately computed for heaviest and lightest girls.

Chapter 5

THE EFFECT OF INTENSIVE PHYSICAL TRAINING UPON BODY COMPOSITION AND PHYSICAL EFFICIENCY OF ADOLESCENT GIRLS

MAGNITUDE OF TISSUE CHANGES DUE TO PHYSICAL TRAINING

T HE EVIDENCE so far presented indicates that exercise exerts a mofidying influence upon the proportional representation in the total body mass of lean tissue and excess fat. Body composition of adequately fed individuals who indulge in physical training is decisively influenced by the amount, nature and intensity of their muscular activities. It is of considerable importance to arrive at an estimate of the magnitude of the tissue changes thus brought about. The data collected during the Kentucky Physical Fitness Experiment allow such an estimate to be made.

In the preceding chapters it was shown that significant gains of lean tissue and significant losses of excess fat occurred in 34 adolescent girls as a result of a 4 1/2 months period of daily physical training. No comparable changes were noted in an inactive control group. A decline of body weight took place during the training in the heaviest girls whose fat losses exceeded their gains of lean tissue; while a correspondingly opposite response was in evidence in the lightest girls.

PERCENTAGE CHANGES OF BODY COMPOSITION IN RELATION TO PERFORMANCE

Fig. 39 (1 and 2) shows the decrease of excess fat and the increase of active tissue at the conclusion of the training experiment as percentages of body weight and of pre-experimental data, respectively. No corresponding changes were noted in the control

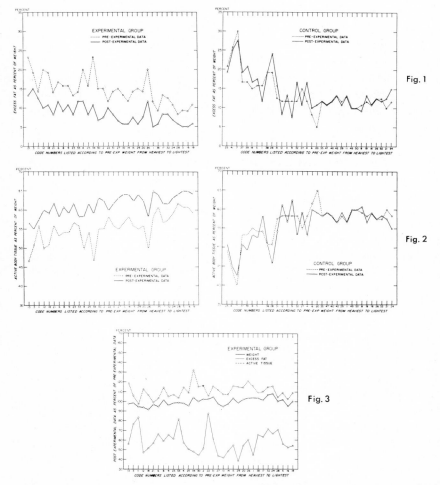

Fig. 39. Presentation of pre- and post-experimental data for excess fat (Fig. 1) and active body tissue (Fig. 2) in exercised and control group. The computed tissue values are expressed as percent of weight. The statistically highly significant differences of the post-experimental measurements are evident. In Figure 3, the post-experimental data of weight, excess fat and active tissue obtained with the exercised group are plotted as percent of the pre-experimental assessments. (Each circle represents a value computed for an individual subject from whom measurements were taken before and after the 4½ months training, as well as from the subjects of the inactive control group. The data thus reflect individual and group trends for the two groups of 34 girls each.)

group. The adjustments of body composition due to training are summarized in Figure 39 (3). Percentagewise, losses of body fat were greater than gains of active tissue. Since the body contains more active tissue than excess fat, mean weight remained relatively constant. Figures 40 and 41 show the girls' performances in two exercise tests, viz., weight lifting and a combined speed and skill event, before and after training. After the training most of the girls were as good or better than the majority of the untrained boys. The overall improvement of the girls' physical efficiency with training is to be considered a functional equivalent

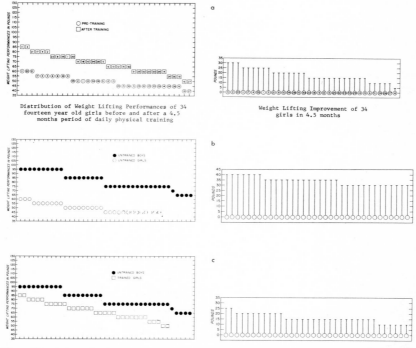

Fig. 40. (a) Distribution of weight lifting performances of 34 14-year old girls before and after a 4.5 months period of daily physical training (left: crude data, plotted in descending sequence; right: performance improvements for each girl). (b) Distribution of weight lifting performances of untrained girls compared with corresponding performances of untrained boys of same age. (c) Distribution of weight lifting performances of same girls after 4.5 months of daily physical training compared with corresponding performances of untrained boys of same age. (b) and (c): left: crude data; right: performance differences between boys and girls.

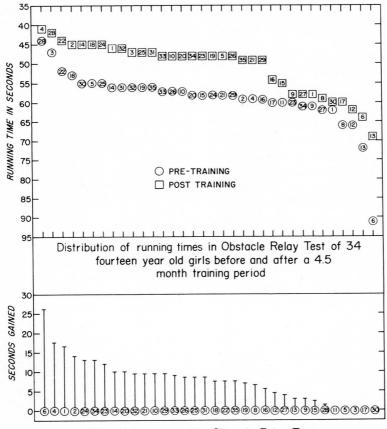

Distribution of running times in Obstacle Relay Test of 34 fourteen year old girls before and after a 4.5 month training period

Rate of improvement in Obstacle Relay Test

Fig. 41

of the tissue changes under reference. The inhibiting influence of excess fat upon physical efficiency has thus been rendered quantitatively identifiable.

EVALUATION OF EFFICIENCY OF GROWING CHILDREN

In order to evaluate the effect of physical training upon performances of growing children, it is necessary to take recourse to grids of performance growth equivalent to those now available on *physical growth*. The former are as necessary for the evaluation of functional determinants of growth as the latter are for the evaluation of anthropometric determinants of growth.

Performance grids differ from growth grids, e.g., grids of height, weight, body fat, lean tissue and other anthropometric parameters. Growth grids allow identification of a number of functional trends some of which reflect secondary sex characteristics that have no morphological equivalents. For example, endurance of untrained girls declines after age 14; while growth of endurance in untrained boys continues. (Fig. 42). Figures 43 (a) and (b) depict performance distribution in a large sample of boys and girls in the 600 yards race. Differential trends, scatter, as well as overlapping fields at various age levels are recognizable. However, the inherent limitations of the quantitative approach to the study of physical efficiency must be kept in mind. To illustrate, reference is made to the fact that while the running-times of the girls at age 14 in the test under review were better than those of girls of 10, the latter were less fatigued after the race than the former; and that the 6 year olds did not look upon the race as particularly strenuous though the girls aged 18 found it exhaustive, (Fig. 44).

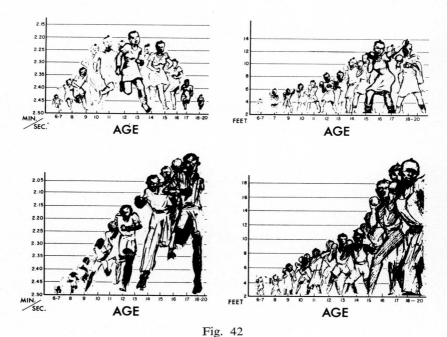

Fig. 42

MENARCHE AS DETERMINANT OF GROWTH AND PERFORMANCE

The extent to which physiological growth changes modify physical performances was shown in an experiment with two groups of 13 year old girls, the one post-, the other pre-menarcheal. The

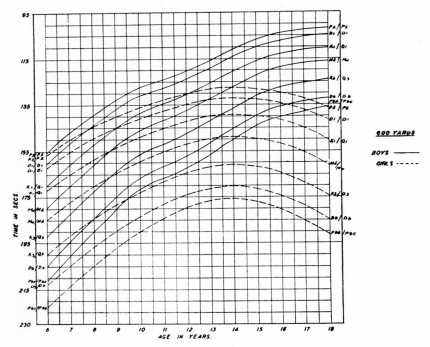

Fig. 43. (a) Performance growth grids constructed from 1514 600 yards running tests conducted with untrained boys and girls of between 6 and 18 years of age. The data were computed and plotted according to the following recording pattern (from top to bottom): 5th percentile, 1st decile, 1st quartile, median, 3rd quartile, 9th decile, 95th percentile. The different developmental trends for boys and girls are evident. As far as running endurance is concerned, physiological "old age" in girls begins at age 14. (b) Comparison of least efficient (3rd quartile, 9th decile and 95th percentile) boys with most efficient (5th percentile, 1st decile and 1st quartile) girls of between 6 and 18 years of age. In any given large sample of children, the best performances of girls are equal or superior to those of a large number of boys. This observation is even more evident if the 1st and last 5 percentile values are retained. The former include the athletically most gifted subjects in whom sustained training will produce a highly significant additional efficiency gain.

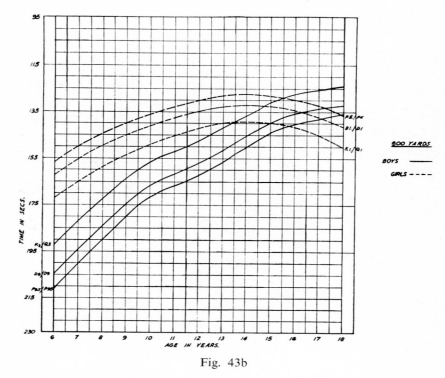

Fig. 43b

former were taller, heavier and fatter; their performances better in the shotput but poorer in the 600 yards race; the discrepancies being equivalent to 1 1/2 years of mean growth between 12 and 14.

THE SIGNIFICANCE OF BODY WEIGHT

We have analyzed the results of 1514 tests of strength, speed and endurance with boys and girls who were divided into three groups, viz., normal weight, underweight and overweight. The heaviest children were strongest but had least endurance (Fig. 45). The relationship between physique and performance is demonstrable most clearly with highly trained subjects in whom the general inhibitory influence upon physical efficiency of excess fat is eliminated. The average weight of the 6 best male shot putters at the Olympic Games in Rome in 1960 was 111.0 kg as against 61.8 kg for the 6 best marathon runners (Fig. 46); and 89.2 kg for the 6 best women shot putters as against 58.5 kg for the six best women middle distance runners.

THE NOTATION OF MOVEMENTS

Mention is made once more of the need to arrive at a system of notation of exercise movements such as in calisthenics, apparatus

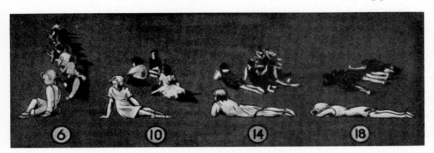

Fig. 44. Fatigue after standardized performance tests of endurance is not necessarily reflected in standard measurements of the subjects' performances. Irrespective of the running times for girls of different ages (Fig. 43 A) the youngest children (6 years of age) were generally the ones who were least exhausted after the 600 yards running test. With increasing age the girls became more and more fatigued. However, it is important to note that the study under review was conducted with untrained subjects.

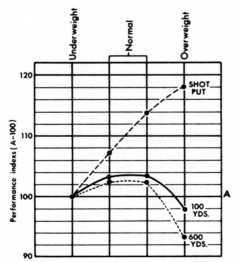

Fig. 45. Analysis of results of 1514 tests of strength, speed and endurance for heavy, normal and light children. Heavy children are strongest but have poor endurance, graded according to standardized percentage scale. (Study conducted with untrained children.)

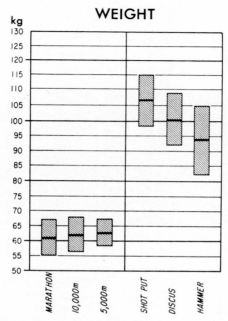

Fig. 46. Body weight of the six best performers in long distance running and throwing contests at Olympic Games in Rome in 1960.

gymnastics, swimming, games etc. (Fig. 47). The latter differ categorically from those customarily employed in laboratory studies, e.g., running the treadmill, riding stationary bicycles, or other ergometric devices. Appropriate beginnings have been made in choreography and music. Notation of group and individual dancing movements have been in use since the 17th Century (Fig. 48). Laban has recently elaborated a new system of symbolic recordings (Fig. 49). The intricacy of neuro-motor activities involved in sport and physical education does not mitigate against the prospect of a successful solution of the problem. After all, the score of symphonic works contains staff notation for each instrument as well as for the relationship between the various elements of the orchestra in its entirety.

Summary

Intensive physical training produces within a few months major changes in body composition. Loss of excess fat and gain in lean tissue before and after training have been estimated as percent of body weight; and the post-experimental data were computed as percent of their pre-experimental correspondents. It is held that criteria of description of exercise procedures as well as of evaluation of results of physical efficiency tests must further be developed. Specifically, it is proposed that studies of the following kind be conducted with a view to arrive at a better understanding of the functional implications of the changes of body composition with physical training:

(1) the elaboration of grids of performance growth for exercise activities of various kind to be applied in the evaluation of

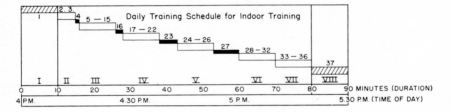

Fig. 47. In order to lay down a concisely defined activity pattern for each exercise period we have prepared a diagrammatic procedure of notation of time sequences for the various activities to be used from day to day. The above illustration which covers a lesson of 1½ hours serves as an example. It reads as follows.

I	(1)	Changing into gymnastic attire
II	(2) and (3)	Warming up activities*
	(4)	Pause
III	(5) - (15)	Calisthenic exercises*
	(16)	Pause. Build up of gymnastic equipment.
IV	(17) - (22)	Apparatus gymnastics*
	(23)	Walk to pool and change into swimsuits
V	(24) - (26)	Organized swimming*
	(27)	Changing into gymnastic attire
VI	(28) - (32)	Weight lifting*
VII	(33) - (36)	Organized games
VIII	(37)	Dressing room

---

*For each individual exercise to be executed in a given class the teacher is referred to a variety of alternatives and combinations as described in textbooks which identify the curriculum in its entirety.

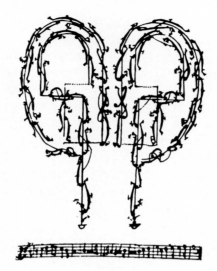

Fig. 48. Steps of a 17th Century dance depicted in choreographic notation devised by Luigi Manzotti (1675-1730).

the functional equivalentss of body composition;

(2) correlation studies of physique and performance, in trained and in untrained subjects;

(3) the development of a system of staff notation for human movements.

REFERENCES

Jokl, E., Cluver, E. H., Goedvolk, C., and deJongh, T. W.: *Training and Efficiency.* Johannesburg, South Africa Institute for Medical Research, 1941.

Jokl, E., and Cluver, E. H.: Physical Fitness. *J.A.M.A.,* May 1941.

Jokl, E.: Body Weight as Determinator of Physical Efficiency. *Nature,* London, December 1944.

Jokl, E., Botha, J. F., and Clark, Daphne: A comparative study of clinical status, standards of growth and of physical performance for 1,439 South African Bantu school children. *South African Medical Journal,* October, 1945.

Jokl, E., Cluver, E. H., and Rorich, P. R.: The physique of American, Canadian, English and South African school children. *South African Journal of Medical Sciences, 11*:45-49, 1946.

Jokl, E., and Cluver, E. H.: Medical Research in Physical Education in South Africa. *Research Quarterly,* March 1949.

Alphabet of Basic Symbols

Variations in the drawing of certain symbols as used by some European colleagues have been included in this alphabet in order to facilitate reading scores. These have been marked "alternate version."

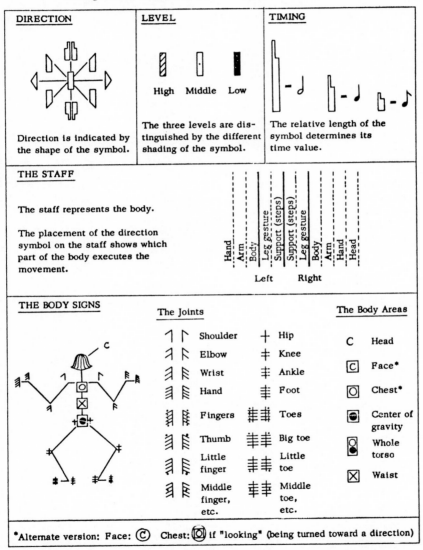

Fig. 49. "Alphabet of Basic Symbols" for gymnastic and dance movements devised by Rudolf Laban in 1954.

Jokl, E., Wells, John B., and Parizkova, Jana: Fitness and Fatness. *J. Phys. Ment. Rehab., 16*:1, 3-7, 23, Jan.-Feb. 1962.

Jokl, E., Wells, John B., and Parizkova, Jana: Exercise, Excess Fat and Body Weight. *J. Phys. Ment. Rehab., 16*:2, 35-40, March-April 1962.

Jokl, E., Wells, John B., and Parizkova, Jana: The Kentucky Physical Fitness Experiment. *J. Phys. Ment. Rehab., 16*:3, 69-72, May-June 1962.

Jokl, E., Wells, John B., and Parizkova, Jana: Growth, Body Composition and Physical Efficiency. *J. Phys. Ment. Rehab.,* 1963.

Jokl, E.: Nutrition and Athletic Performance. *Netherlands Journal of Nutrition, 23*:11, November 1962.

Haskell, Arnold L.: *The Story of Dance.* Rathbone, London, 1960.

Hutchinson, Ann: *Labanotation.* New Directions Books, New York, 1954.

Morris, Margaret: *The Notation of Movement.* Kegan, Paul, Trench, Trubner & Co., London, 1928.

Wolf, Johannes: *Die Tonschriften.* Ferdinand Hirt, Breslau, 1924.

(A noteworthy publication in which the present knowledge of body composition is well detailed is contained in the two volumes of the *Annals of the New York Academy of Sciences, 110,* pp. 1-424, and 425-1018, published in 1963 under the editorship of Josef Brozek.)

Chapter 6

STATISTICAL TREATMENT OF BODY MEASUREMENTS IN RELATION TO GROWTH AND PHYSICAL TRAINING AS MODIFYING INFLUENCES

THE GROWTH FACTOR

Since the Kentucky Physical Fitness Experiment had a duration of 4 1/2 months, consideration had to be given to the normal growth of girls between the ages of 14 and 16 years, with special reference to the changes in body weight, excess fat and active tissue. In order to assess the effect of the exercise curriculum, this "growth factor" had to be extrapolated. The following method of calculation was employed with this aim in view:

The "Standard Grid for Height and Weight of Girls" constructed by Jokl *et al.,* from a large random sample was used as a basis to obtain straight line approximations of average percentage increases of body weight per month between the ages of 14 and 16 years. At age 13, the average girl weighs 98 pounds; at age 16, 122 pounds. Thus, a mean increase of 24 pounds or 24.49 per cent in body weight occurs in 36 months, or a mean increase of 3 pounds or 3.06 per cent in 4 1/2 months. Corresponding analyses demonstrated that the heaviest girls in this age group would have a mean increase due to growth of 2.77 pounds or 2.45 per cent. The lightest girls averaged a mean increase of 3.29 pounds or 5.21 per cent body weight during the 4 1/2 months. Having thus determined mean increases in total body weight due to normal growth for heavy, average and light girls of the age level under study, it was necessary to determine what part of this increase was due to normal growth of excess fat, of active tissue and of bone and essential fat. Data are available upon which the required computations can be based. For example, in her study, "The Development of Subcutaneous Fat in Normal and Obese Children," J. Parizkova found that mean abdominal skinfold thicknesses of 13 year old girls were 19 mm, while at age 16 mean values of 23.2 mm were found, indicating an increase of 4.2 mm in three years, or 22.11 per cent. For the 4 1/2 months period of the Kentucky Physical Fitness Experiment, a mean increase in abdominal skinfold thicknesses of 0.52 mm or 2.75 per cent was therefore accepted as basic growth equivalent. Using the relationship determined in our previous paper

$$y = 1.0828 - .00134 \; x$$

where y is body density of average girls and x skinfold thickness, it was found that the body density of average girls age 13 is 1.0573 and at age 16, 1.0517. Applying the formula of Keys and Brozek to determine the per cent of excess fat from body density, it was ascertained that the average untrained girl age 13 had 15.68 pounds or 16.0 per cent and at age 16, 22.08 pounds or 18.1 per cent of body weight as excess fat. This is an increase of 6.40 pounds or 2.1 per cent in 36 months; 0.25 pounds or 0.26 per cent for 4 1/2 months in excess fat due to normal growth.

A similar analysis for the heaviest and lightest girls in this new age group yielded an average increase of 0.24 pounds or 0.21 per cent in excess fat for the heaviest girls and an increase of 0.27 pounds or 0.44 per cent in excess fat for the lightest girls.

Assuming that 30 per cent of total body weight is bone and essential fat, and that 30 per cent of the increase in total body weight is due to a corresponding normal growth of bone and essential fat, bone and essential fat of the heaviest girls increase by 0.84 pounds or 0.74 per cent; of average girls by 0.92 pounds or 0.92 per cent; and of the lightest girls by 0.97 pounds or 1.56 per cent. The remaining increase in total body weight during the 4 1/2 months due to growth of active tissue is 1.70 pounds or 1.50 per cent for the heaviest girls; 1.84 pounds for 1.88 per cent for the average girls; and 1.99 pounds or 3.21 per cent for the lightest girls.

TABLE I

AVERAGE PERCENT INCREASE DUE TO GROWTH FOR GIRLS FROM 13 TO 16 YEARS OF AGE
FOR A 4½ MONTHS PERIOD

Factor	Heaviest Girls		Average Girls		Lightest Girls	
	Per cent	Pounds	Per cent	Pounds	Per cent	Pounds
Bone and Essential Fat	0.74	0.84	0.92	0.90	1.56	0.97
Excess Fat	0.21	0.24	0.26	0.25	0.44	0.27
Active Tissue	1.50	1.70	1.88	1.84	3.21	1.99
Total Body Weight	2.45	2.77	3.06	3.00	5.21	3.23

Measurements of height were made both before and after the experiment. Increases during the 4 1/2 months were very small and could be disregarded for purposes of our present study. No significant differences in height and in growth of height were revealed by our data for the two groups of girls.

METHODOLOGICAL CONSIDERATIONS

Students' t-test was applied to test various hypotheses concerning the mean percentage values and mean percentage differences of the two groups of 34 girls, experimental and control before and after removal of the "growth factor." Table 2 summarizes the results of the tests of hypotheses. The 0.05 level of significance was assumed for purposes of interpretation of the results described in the following.

To test values between the two groups, t was computed by the formula:

$$(1) \quad t = \frac{M_2 - M_1}{\sqrt{(n_1-1) S_1^2 + (N_2-1)S_2^2}} \sqrt{\frac{n_1 n_2 \ (n_1 + n_2 - 2)}{n_1 + n_2}}$$

where M_1 and M_2 are the means of the two groups; S_1^2 and S_2^2 the corresponding variances; n_1 and n_2 the corresponding sample sizes; and $n_1 + n_2 - 2$ is the number of degrees of freedom.

For testing values within a group, the observations were paired and t was computed from the formula:

$$(2) \quad t = \frac{D \sqrt{n}}{S_D}$$

where D is the mean difference, n is the sample size, S_D is the standard deviation and n-1 is the number of degrees of freedom.

t was determined in such a manner that its value was always

TABLE 2

Test of Hypotheses on:	Hypotheses tested	dof_1	Body Weight t	p	Lean Tissue t	p	Excess Fat t	p
Groups of 34 Girls	$H_0: M_1 = M_2$ / $H_1: M_1 \neq M_2$	66			0.94	.3<p<.4	0.95	.3<p<.4
	$H_0: M_1' = M_2'$ / $H_1: M_1' \neq M_2'$	66			5.85[a]	p<.001	6.07[a]	p<.001
	$H_0: M_1^* = O$ / $H_1: M_1^* \neq O$	33	0.30	p>.5	9.59[a]	p<.001	20.29[a]	p<.001
	$H_0: M_2^* = O$ / $H_1: M_2^* \neq O$	33	1.39	.1<p<.2	0.22	p>.5	1.71	.05<p<.1
	$H_0: M_1^{**} = O$ / $H_1: M_1^{**} \neq O$	33	4.32[a]	p<.001	6.34[a]	p<.001	18.91[a]	p<.001
	$H_0: M_2^{**} = O$ / $H_1: M_2^{**} \neq O$	33	3.52[b]	.001<p<.005	3.06[b]	.001<p<.005	1.19	.2<p<.3
11 Heaviest Girls	$H_0: M_1 = M_2$ / $H_1: M_1 \neq M_2$	20			1.15	.2<p<.3	1.06	.3<p<.4
	$H_0: M_1' = M_2'$ / $H_1: M_1' \neq M_2'$	20			5.39[a]	p<.001	5.82[a]	p<.001
	$H_0: M_1^* = O$ / $H_1: M_1^* \neq O$	10	4.09[b]	.001<p<.005	3.92[b]	.001<p<.005	10.30[a]	p<.001
	$H_0: M_2^* = O$ / $H_1: M_2^* \neq O$	10	0.08	p>.5	0.59	p>.5	1.35	.1<p<.2
	$H_0: M_1^{**} = O$ / $H_1: M_1^{**} \neq O$	10	7.10[a]	p<.001	2.91[d]	.01<p<.025	10.67[a]	p<.001
	$H_0: M_2^{**} = O$ / $H_1: M_2^{**} \neq O$	10	1.81	.1<p<.2	1.58	.1<p<.2	1.07	.2<p<.3
11 Lightest Girls	$H_0: M_1 = M_2$ / $H_1: M_1 \neq M_2$	20			0.29	p>.5	0.38	p>.5
	$H_0: M_1' = M_2'$ / $H_1: M_1' \neq M_2'$	20			4.87[a]	p<.001	6.29[a]	p<.001
	$H_0: M_1^* = O$ / $H_1: M_1^* \neq O$	10	2.75[d]	.01<p<.025	7.42[a]	p<.001	16.84[a]	p<.001
	$H_0: M_2^* = O$ / $H_1: M_2^* \neq O$	10	1.00	.3<p<.4	0.15	p<.5	6.17[a]	p<.001
	$H_0: M_1^{**} = O$ / $H_1: M_1^{**} \neq O$	10	2.58[e]	.025<p<.05	2.99[e]	.01<p<.025	10.93[a]	p<.001
	$H_0: M_2^{**} = O$ / $H_1: M_2^{**} \neq O$	10	7.87[a]	p<.001	7.89[a]	p<.001	0.66	.4<p<.5

1: degrees of freedom
a: significance at .001 confidence level
b: significance at .005 confidence level
c: significance at .010 confidence level
d: significance at .025 confidence level
e: significance at .050 confidence level

TABLE 3

			Pre-study % of body wt.	Pre-study lbs.	Post-study % of body wt.	Post-study lbs.	% Of Gain or Loss pct.	% Of Gain or Loss lbs.	After Removal of Growth Factor % of body wt.	After Removal of Growth Factor lbs.	% Of Gain or Loss pct.	% Of Gain or Loss lbs.
Group of 34 Girls	Experimental Group	Lean Tissue	55.3	63.8	61.4	70.7	10.9	6.9	61.8	68.6	7.5	4.8
		Excess Fat	14.7	17.5	8.6	10.3	-41.4	-7.2	8.9	10.0	-41.9	-7.5
	Control Group	Lean Tissue	56.3	66.2	55.6	66.0	-0.2	-0.2	54.4	64.1	-3.3	-2.1
		Excess Fat	13.7	17.0	14.4	17.8	6.1	0.8	15.3	17.7	4.3	0.7
11 lightest Girls	Experimental Group	Lean Tissue	58.2	56.6	63.2	63.1	11.6	6.5	63.1	59.9	5.2	3.3
		Excess Fat	11.8	11.6	6.8	7.0	-40.1	-4.6	6.9	6.9	-41.0	-4.7
	Control Group	Lean Tissue	58.6	58.7	58.2	58.6	-0.1	-0.1	58.6	55.5	-5.6	-3.2
		Excess Fat	11.4	11.4	11.8	11.8	4.2	0.4	11.4	11.8	0.3	0.4
11 heaviest Girls	Experimental Group	Lean Tissue	53.1	72.1	58.9	77.6	7.0	5.5	58.8	75.6	4.8	3.5
		Excess Fat	16.9	23.3	11.1	14.7	-36.8	-8.6	11.0	14.2	-37.2	-9.1
	Control Group	Lean Tissue	51.2	72.8	50.3	71.9	-1.3	-0.9	48.1	70.4	-3.4	-2.4
		Excess Fat	18.8	27.3	19.7	28.3	6.3	1.0	21.8	28.0	5.1	0.7

positive, in table 2 H_0 stands for the null hypothesis being tested, H_1 stands for the alternative hypothesis. M_1 and M_2 stand for the mean percentages of the experimental and control groups, respectively, at the beginning of the experiment. M_1^1 and M_2^1 denote the same values at the end of the experimental period. M^*_1 and M^*_2 stand for the mean percentage gains of the experimental and control groups before the growth factor is removed; while M_1^{**} and M_2^{**} stands for the corresponding values after the growth factor has been removed.

The following is a summary of the results of the computation of the effect of the physical training upon body composition.

COMPARATIVE ANALYSIS OF DATA FOR 34 GIRLS OF EXPERIMENTAL GROUP AND 34 GIRLS OF CONTROL GROUP

Lean Tissue

At the beginning of the study lean tissue for the experimental group averaged 63.80 pounds or 55.3 per cent of body weight. For the control group this value was 66.17 pounds or 56.3 per cent. This indicated that the two groups did not differ significantly in this factor at the beginning of the experiment. At the end of the study, the lean tissue of the experimental group averaged 70.70 pounds or 61.4 per cent of body weight while this value for the control group was now 66.04 pounds or 55.6 per cent. Hence there was at this stage a significant difference in the average ratio of lean tissue to total body weight. The experi-

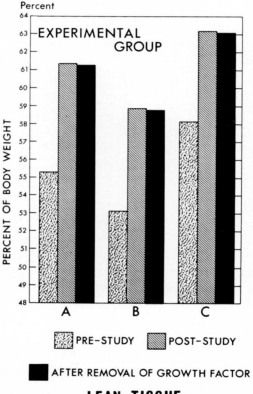

LEAN TISSUE

Figs. 50 and 51. Percentage representation of lean tissue and of excess fat in two groups of 34 adolescent girls before and after a 4½ months study. (A) Means of measurements for 34 girls. (B) Means of measurements for 11 heaviest girls. (C) Means of measurements for 11 lightest girls. Note the marked increase of lean tissue. Correspondingly, opposite adaptive changes were in evidence in respect of excess fat.

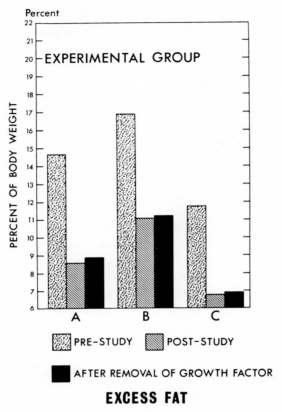

Fig. 51

mental group gained on the average 6.90 pounds or 10.9 per cent in tissue which was a significant increase. The control group lost on the average 0.2 pounds or 0.2 per cent lean tissue. This is not a significant loss. When the factor of normal growth was taken into consideration, the experimental group gained on the average 4.80 pounds or 7.49 per cent in lean tissue which is also significant. The control group lost on the average 2.14 pounds or 3.34 per cent in lean tissue when the growth factor was considered which is a significant loss. We conclude that while the average ratio of lean tissue to body weight for the two groups did not differ significantly at the beginning of the study, the experimental group gained a significant percentage of lean tissue during the period of training, while the inactive control group lost significantly in this respect.

Excess Fat

At the beginning of the study excess fat for the experimental group averaged 17.50 pounds or 14.7 per cent of total body weight; for the control group this value was 17.0 pounds or 13.7 per cent. This showed that the two groups did not differ significantly. At the end of the study the average excess fat of the experimental group was 10.30 pounds or 8.6 per cent of body weight while this value for the control group was 17.80 pounds or 14.4 per cent. Hence there was a significant difference. The experimental group lost an average of 7.20 pounds or 41.4 per cent in excess fat, a highly significant amount. The control group gained an average of 0.80 pounds or 6.1 per cent in excess fat which was not significant. When the growth factor was considered, the experimental group lost on the average 7.50 pounds or 41.93 per cent in excess fat which is very significant. The control group gained an average of 0.70 pounds or 4.34 per cent in excess fat which is not significant. We conclude that while the average ratio of excess fat to body weight for the two groups did not differ significantly at the beginning of the experiment, the experimental group lost a highly significant amount of excess fat while the control group showed no significant changes.

Body Weight

During the study the experimental group lost .23 pounds or 0.2 per cent in body weight while the control group gained .95 pounds or 0.8 per cent. Neither of these changes were significant. When the factor of normal growth was taken into consideration, the weight loss for the experimental group amounted to 3.96 pounds or 3.71 per cent and for the control group 3.26 pounds or 2.74 per cent. The difference between these two amounts is insignificant. The relevance of taking into account in all studies of the effect of physical training upon body weight absolute and relative starting levels has been pointed out in the preceding communication of this series: "The Kentucky Physical Fitness Experiment" (2).

COMPARATIVE ANALYSIS OF DATA FOR 11 HEAVIEST GIRLS OF EXPERIMENTAL GROUP AND 11 HEAVIEST GIRLS OF CONTROL GROUP

Lean Tissue

At the beginning of the experiment the 11 heaviest girls of the experimental group on the average had 72.10 pounds or 53.1 per cent of their body weight in the form of lean tissue while for the control group this value was 72.80 pounds or 51.2 per cent. The difference between the two groups was not significant. At the end of the experiment the 11 heaviest girls of the experimental group on the average had 77.60 pounds or 58.9 per cent of their body weight in the form of lean tissue while for the control group this value was 71.90 pounds or 50.3 per cent. At the end of the study the two groups thus differed significantly. The average per-cent of gain in lean tissue for the 11 heaviest girls in the experimental group was 5.5 pounds or 7.0 per cent; or 3.5 pounds or 4.8 per cent gain after that part which is due to normal growth is removed. The corresponding values for the control group were a loss of 0.90 pounds or 1.3 per cent; or 2.4 pounds or 3.4 per cent after the growth factor is removed. In either case, the experimental group's average gain in active tissue was significant; while such changes as occurred in the control group were in both cases not significant.

Excess Fat

At the beginning of the study the 11 heaviest girls of the experimental group on the average had 23.3 pounds or 16.9 per cent of their body weight in the form of excess fat; while for the 11 heaviest girls of the control group this value was 27.3 pounds or 18.8 per cent. The difference was not significant. At the end of the study the 11 heaviest girls of the experimental group had on the average 14.70 pounds or 11.1 per cent of their body weight in the form of excess fat; while for the control group this value was 28.30 pounds or 19.7 per cent. The difference between the two groups was now significant. The average per cent of loss in excess fat for the 11 heaviest girls in the experimental group was 8.60 pounds or 36.8 percent; or 9.20 pounds or 37.2 percent after that part which is due to normal growth is removed. The corresponding values for the control group were a gain of 1.00 pound or 6.3 percent, or 0.70 pound or 5.1 percent after the growth factor is removed. In either cases the experimental group's average percentage loss in excess fat was significant while such changes as occurred in the control group were not significant.

Body Weight

During the experimental period the 11 heaviest girls in the experimental group actually lost 4.72 pounds or 3.3 percent in total body weight. When the growth factor is taken into consideration this group lost 7.75 pounds or 5.7 percent of total body weight. In both cases this group showed a significant loss of body weight. During the same time, the control group gained an average of 0.23 pounds or 0.1 percent in body weight and when the growth factor was considered this value became a loss of 3.19 pounds or 2.3 percent. The actual gain by the control group was not significant and when normal growth is considered we find that the loss by the control group is also not significant.

COMPARATIVE ANALYSIS OF DATA FOR 11 LIGHTEST GIRLS OF EXPERIMENTAL GROUP AND 11 LIGHTEST GIRLS OF CONTROL GROUP

Lean Tissue

At the beginning of the study the 11 lightest girls of the experimental group on the average had 56.60 pounds or 58.2 percent of their body weight in the form of lean tissue; while for the control group this value was 58.70 or 58.6 percent. The difference was not significant. At the end of the study, the 11 lightest girls of the experimental group on the average had 63.10 pounds or 63.2 percent of their body weight in the form of lean tissue; while for the control group this value was 58.60 pounds or 58.2 percent. Thus, at the end of the study, the two groups differed significantly. The average percent of gain in lean tissue for the 11 lightest girls in the experimental group was 6.50 pounds or 11.6 percent; or 3.30 pounds or 5.2 percent after that part which is due to normal growth is removed. The corresponding values for the control group were a loss of 0.10 pounds or 0.1 percent; or 3.20 pounds or 5.6 percent after the growth factor is removed. In either case, the experimental group's average gain in active tissue was significant. In the control group the loss was significant only after removal of the growth factor.

Excess Fat

At the beginning of the study the 11 lightest girls of the experimental group on the average had 11.60 pounds or 11.8 percent of their body weight in the form of excess fat; while for the control group this value was 11.40 pounds or 11.4 percent. The difference was not significant. At the end of the study, the 11 lightest girls of the experimental group on the average had 7.0 pounds or 6.8 percent of their body weight in the form of excess fat; while for the control group, this value was 11.80 pounds or 11.80 percent. Thus, the two groups differed significantly. The average percent of loss in excess fat for the 11 lightest girls in the experimental group was 4.60 pounds or 40.1 percent; or 4.70 pounds or 41.0 percent after that part which is due to normal growth is removed. The corresponding values for the control group were a gain of 0.40 pounds or 4.2 percent; or a gain of 0.30 pounds or 0.3 percent after the growth factor is removed. In either case the experimental group's average loss in excess fat was significant; while in the control group such changes as occurred lost their significance after removal of the growth factor.

Body Weight

During the experimental period the 11 lightest girls in the experimental group actually gained 2.86 pounds or 2.7 percent in total body weight. When the growth factor is taken into consideration this group lost 2.38 pounds or 2.5 percent in total body weight. The actual percentage gain shown was significant and after the removal of the growth factor this became a significant loss. During the same time, the control group gained an average of 0.50 pounds or 0.6 percent in body weight and if the growth factor is considered this value is a loss of 4.72 pounds or 4.7 percent in total body weight. The actual gain by the control group was not significant but when the growth factor is considered the loss observed becomes a significant loss.

SUMMARY AND CONCLUSIONS

In assessing the effects of training upon morphological and functional characteristics of children, the growth factor must be taken into account. The analysis of the evidence on body composition obtained during the Kentucky Physical Fitness Experiment allowed an estimate of the differences between "crude" and "corrected" data. Percentage representations of excess fat and lean tissue in an experimental and a control group of 34 adolescent girls were compared prior to and at the end of the 4 1/2 months study before and after removal of the growth factor. The statistical principle of extrapolation applied in these computations is of importance in all longitudinal researches on exercise and physical development.

The discovery now confirmed beyond doubt that inactivity facilitates the deposition of excess fat and inhibits muscular development renders feasible a further differentiation of analyses of the effects of physical training. The traditional method of anthropometric surface examination of trained and untrained subjects of different somatotypes can now be supplemented by quantitative determinations of various fractions of body tissue and of body water. Thus, a new morphological concept of fitness is emerging and with it new possibilities of correlating a number of previously unknown anatomical equivalents to performance measurements in terms of cardiovascular, respiratory, metabolic and thermo-regulatory adaptations to exercise and training. The integrative function of the nervous system in exercise is thus also becoming amenable to a progressively sharper identification in its multiple projections in the neuro-muscular, the autonomic and throphic sectors.

AUTHOR INDEX

Albertyn, J. R., 51
Alexander, J. K., vi, 16, 29, 37
Allen, T. H., 65, 70
Amad, K. H., 37
Aristotle, 13
Armstrong, Donald, 29, 37
Austin, R., 37

Behnke, A. R., vi, 53, 55-56, 58-59, 70
Belknap, E. K., 38-39
Berry, W. T. C., 37
Beveridge, J. B., 37
Bland, E. F., 37
Bohanan, J., 40
Bond, E. E., 71
Bonnet, E. C., 37
Bonneth, 29
Botha, J. F., 94
Boxer, G. E., 18, 39
Bramwell, M., 37
Bransby, E. R., 37
Brozek, Josef, vi, 45, 52, 57, 59-61, 65, 70-71, 98
Bruch, Hilde, vi, 45, 52
Brukhardt, 29
Brunner, Daniel, 14, 30, 37, 81, 83
Bullen, B., 38
Buskirk, E. R., vi, 60-61, 64, 71
Bustos, J., 42, 52

Cady, L. D., 27, 37
Calvy, G. L., 27-28, 37
Carns, M. L., 39
Chalmers, A. K., 37
Chang, C. W., 70
Chen, K. P., 70
Chester, 42
Chirico, Anna-Marie, 47, 52, 69, 71
Christensen, E. H., 37
Clark, Daphne, 94

Cluver, E. H., 41, 52, 55, 70, 94
Crawford, M. D., 39
Curtius, F., 30, 37
Curtius, N., vi

Dale, J. H., 42, 52
Dalton, 34
Daubney, C. G., 37
de Jongh, T. W., 41, 52, 55, 70, 94
Dennis, E. W., 37
Deuel, H. J., Jr., 37
Diettert, G. A., 37
Dorris, R. J., 48, 52
Driskel, M. M., 37
Dublin, L. I., 29, 37
Duncan, W. C., 37

Einstein, 34
Eisenbeisser, H. E., 39
Elliot, 18
Eberl, J., 39
Esser, E., 40

Faller, I. L., 71
Fang, H. S., 70
Faulhorn, 16
Feen, B. G., 70
Fertig, J., 37
Fick, 16
Fletcher, W. M., 18, 37
Frankel, T., 71
Freeman, S., 71
Friedmann, R., 39
Frucht, A. H., 17, 36-37

Garland, P. B., 39
Garns, S. M., 37
Gertler, M. M., 27, 29, 37

109

Gilmore, R. C., 39
Glatzel, H., 17, 37
Goedvolk, C., 52, 94
Grosskopf, J. F. W, 51
Grossman, M. I., 71
Gunkler, O., 71

Halac, J., 38
Hales, C. N., 39
Hanfmann, E, 52
Hansen, O., 37
Hardy, J. A., 39
Haskell, Arnold L., 96
Hellebrandt, F. A., 39
Hendrick, E., 37
Hill, A. V., 18, 36-37
Hindhede, M., 17, 37
Holt, L E., 16, 38
Hopkins, F. G., 18, 37
Huang, T. F., 70
Hutchinson, Ann, 96

Johnson, H., 40
Johnson, Warren R., 71
Jokl, Ernst, v, 4, 7, 31, 38, 40-41, 44,
52, 55-56, 70, 94, 96-97
Jongh, T. W. de, 41, 52, 55, 70, 94

Kajdi, C. N., 38
Karpinos, B. D., 79
Karvonen, M., vi, 3-4, 11-13, 30-31, 35,
38-39
Keller, W. D., 18, 38
Keys, Ancel, vi, 5, 9-12, 17, 38-39, 45,
52, 57, 59-61, 65, 70-71, 81, 83, 98
Keys, M., 38
Kihlberg, J., 3, 11-12, 38
Kolkka, S., 38
Konttinen, A., 21, 39
Kopf, H., 38
Koskela, A., 3, 38
Kretschmer, E., 29, 42, 44, 52
Krogh, A., 38

Laban, Rudolf, 92, 95
Lange, Karl, 60, 63
Lerman, J., 37
Levine, S. M., 37
Levinson, D. J., 52
Levy, H., 34, 38
Lindhard, J., 38

Magee, H. E., 37
Malherbe, E. G., 51
Manelis, G., 37
Manzotti, Liugi, 94
Margaria, R., 20
Marks, H. H., 29, 37
Mattill, H. I., 38
Mayer, Jean, vi, 38, 49-50, 52
Mellerowicz, H., 17, 38
Meserve, E. R., 37
Meyerhof, O., 18, 38
Missiuro, W., 62
Moore, R., 71
Morris, J. N., vi, 14, 30, 38-39
Morris, Margaret, 38, 96
Mufson, M. A., 27, 37
Murray, W. A., 51

Needman, B. M., 37
Newsholme, E. A., 39
Newton, 34
Nierman, J., 27, 37
Nikkila, E. A., 21, 28, 39
Noro, L., 3, 38
Nothdurft, H., 39
Nydick, M., 42, 52

Parizkova, Jana, vi, 40, 65, 71, 96, 98
Parks, J. W., 39
Pascale, L. R., vi, 71
Peng, M. T., 70
Pettenkofer, M., von, 18, 39
Pickering, Sir George, 36, 39
Pomeroy, W. C., 13, 39

Raab, W., 39
Raffle, P. A. B., 39
Randell, 22
Randle, P., vi, 39
Rautaharju, P. M., 11, 39
Rautanen, Y., 11-12, 38
Rawson, R. W., 42, 52
Reinecke, R. M., 39
Rikkonen, P., 11-12, 38
Roberts, C. G., 39
Rogers, Terence A., vi, 59, 71
Rook, Sir Alan, 13
Rorich, P. R., 94
Rosenbaum, F. F., 38-39
Rothmann, M. E., 51
Russel, J., 39

Samuels, L. T., 39
Schade, M., 39
Schapiro, B., 40
Scheer, B. T., 37
Schimert, G., 17, 29, 39
Schimmler, W., 39
Schwalb, H., 39
Selye, 36
Shapiro, 20
Sheldon, 29
Siegel, S., 48, 52
Simon, E., 70
Smith, W. G., 37
Smuts, General J. C., 50
Snell, 18
Spain, 29
Sprague, H. B., 37
Starr, I., vi, 8
Stetten, W., 18, 39
Straub, E., 37
Stunkard, A. J., vi, 47-48, 52, 69, 71

Tanner, J. M., 62
Taylor, H. L., 39
Townsend, H. S., 37
Turner, N. C., 37

Voit, 15, 18, 39

Waterland, J. C., 39
Welham, W. C., 70
Wells, John B., vi, 40, 96
Wertheimer, E., 20, 40
White, P. D., 13, 29, 37, 39
Wilcocks, R. W., 51
Wislicenus, 16
Witkowski, M., vi, 40, 62
Wolf, Johannes, 96

Yudkin, John, vi, 6, 14, 40

SUBJECT INDEX

Acids, non-esterified fatty, 21-22, 24
Anti-atherogenic influence of physical training, 13-15
Atherogenic properties of diets, 3
Athletic efficiency, environmental determinants of, 30-33
Athletic performance and nutrition, 3-40

Body
  composition
    performance and, 84-87
    physical efficiency and, 84-96
    physical training and, 84-96
  measurements, growth and physical training as modifying influences, 97-108
Body Fat in Adult Men, 59-62

Caliper, skinfold, 63
Calories
  consumption, and Olympic participation, 31
  intake and thermodynamic output, 17-18
Cardiovascular disease and obesity, 16
Cholesterol, 25
Choreographic notation, 94-95
"Constitutional predisposition," 28-30

Dance notation, 94-95
Diet(s)
  atherogenic properties, 3
  average American citizen, 5
  blood lipids and, 9-13
  ergogenic properties, 3
  ischemic heart disease and, 9-13
  Keys' ideal diet, 5
  Olympic athletes, 5
  proteins and, 15-17
  underprivileged third of world, 5

Efficiency (*see* Physical efficiency)
Environmental determinants of athletic efficiency, 30-33
Enzymes, 27-28
Ergogenic properties of diets, 3
Exercise
  fat and, excess, 53-71
  muscular, fuel of, 18-21
  N.E.F.A. and, 21-22
  nutrition and, 49-50
  triglycerides and, 21-22
  weight and, 53-71
  weight contol and, 49-50

Fat
  adult men and, 59-62
  body water and, 62-64
  content of body, specific gravity of, 53-54
  excess, 103-107
    (*See also* Obesityy)
    circumferential body measurements indicating, 54-59
    exercise and body weight, 53-71
    Kentucky Physical Fitness Experiment and, 76-77
  subcutaneous layers, norms for, 65
Fatigue after performance, 91
Fatty Acids
  glucose cycle, 26
  non-esterified, 21-22, 24
Fitness (*see* Kentucky Physical Fitness Experiment)
Fuel of muscular exercise, 18-21

Glucose fatty-acid cycle, 26
Growth
  as modifying influence on body measurements, 97-108
  menarche and, 89-90

physical efficiency of growing children, 87-88

Health, socio-economic status and physical performance, 4-9
Heart disease
coronary, mortality from, 9
ischemic, 9-13

India
nutritional standards, 3
Olympic performance data, 4

Kentucky Physical Fitness Experiment, 72-83
growth factor during, 97-108
statistical considerations, 72-77

Lipids, 27-28
blood, 9-13

Menarche, 89-90
Mortality, coronary heart disease, 9
Motivation, significance of, 44
Movements, notation of, 33-35, 91-92

N.E.F.A., 24
exercise and, 21-22
Notation of movements, 33-35, 91-92
Nutrition
exercise and, 49-50
performance and, athletic, 3-40
standards in U.S. and India, 3
weight control and, 49-50

Obesity
(*See also* Fat, excess)
cardiovascular disease and, 16
effects of physical training on, 41-44
importance of overweight, 45
personality characteristics of children and, 45-46
physical inactivity causing, 41-52
walking activities and, 47-48
weight control, 49-50

Olympic performance, data for U.S. and India, 4
Overweight (*see* Fat, excess, Obesity)

Performance, athletic, and nutrition, 3-40
body composition and, 84-87
fatigue after, 91
menarche and, 89-90
Olympic, data for U.S. and India, 4
physical, health and socio-economic status, 4-9
Personality characteristics of overweight children, 45-46
Physical efficiency
body composition and training, 84-96
evaluation in growing children, 87-88
Physical fitness (*see* Kentucky Physical Fitness Experiment)
Physical inactivity causing obesity, 41-52
Physical training
anti-atherogenic influence of 13-15
as modifying influence on body measurements, 97-108
body composition and, 84-96
effects on obese and lean subjects, 41-44
physical efficiency and, 84-96
tissue changes due to, 84
"Physical Training Battalion," 50-52
"Poor Whites," 50-52
Proteins, dietary, 15-17

Quantitative method, limitations of, 23-27

"Sexual bimorphism," 65
Skinfold caliper, 63
Socio-economic status, health and physical performance, 4-9
"Stress," 35-36

Thermodynamic output and caloric intake, 17-18
Tissue changes due to training, 84
Training (*see* Physical training)
Triglycerides, 24
exercise and, 21-22

United States
  nutritional standards, 3
  Olympic performance data, 4

Walking activities and obesity, 47-48
Water, body, and body fat, 62-64

Weight, 104, 106-107
  control, 49-50
  exercise and, 53-71
  fat and, excess, 53-71
  Kentucky Physical Fitness Experiment
  and, 75
  significance of, 90-91